THE
R_F
POSTCARD
PRICE GUIDE

compiled by
JOAN VENMAN
and
RON MEAD

Overseas Postcards section by
PAUL KONEC

All illustrations in this price guide are from the stock of R.F. POSTCARDS and
R.F. STAMPS

published by
Richard Stenlake Publishing, Ochiltree Sawmill, The Lade,
Ochiltree, Ayrshire, KA18 2NX. phone/fax 01290 700266

First Published in the United Kingdom, 1995 by Richard Stenlake Publishing
ISBN 1-872074-55-3

Undivided back J.A. Stewart military. £8

PRICING NOTES

There is no price control on postcards. The value of any card is in the eye of the beholder and where a range is quoted in this price guide the reader must use his or her own judgement to decide where any particular card lies taking into account the condition.

In the case of 'art' cards, they should be as near as possible to their original condition when published, cards even slightly damaged could be worth considerably less than a perfect specimen.

With topographical cards, more latitude is allowable.

Terms used in the hobby

APPLIQUE:	Postcards to which some 'material' has been attached etc.
CHROMO-LITHO:	A form of very fine early printing using up to twelve colours.
COMPOSITES:	Several cards making one picture when placed together
DIVIDED BACKS:	A line dividing the back of the card into message and address space. Used in the U.K. from late 1902.
EMBOSSED:	The design raised, usually greetings types.
HOLD TO LIGHT:	(abbreviation: HTL). These are all cards to be looked through against the light. There are three types: a) **Cut-outs:** Portions of the upper layer of the card are removed and the lower layer is coloured and translucent. b&c) **Transparencies:** On holding to light either the colour and/or the scene changes.
MAGIC CARDS:	These reveal a picture when rubbing with a coin, or heat is applied to them.
PULL OUTS:	Where strips of views, etc. are folded under flaps on the face of the cards and 'pulled out' to view.
TUCKS:	Cards published by Raphael Tuck & Son are referred to as 'Tucks' throughout the hobby.
UNDIVIDED BACKS:	Early cards with no space on the address side for message, which was meant to be written on the picture side.
VIGNETTE:	During the undivided back period the small picture or pictures on the face of the card.
WRITE-AWAY:	Card, usually comic, where the message is started for you.

They eventually went Dutch and became Shell-Mex. £30

Good stock. £30

Slightly more unusual Bonzo card. £30

A nice advert. £25

ADVERTISING

Very little first class material is available and interest is concentrated in the specialist areas such as railway, shipping, theatre etc. Advertising is a major collecting category and one of the earliest uses of pictorial postcards, many examples existing which pre-date the earliest permissable dates for *picture* postcards (1894). Examples of advertising on postal stationery postcards with printed stamps are common and are sometimes found with punch or file holes, confirming their commercial use.

POSTERS

Adkins Tobacco, Tom Browne	£125
Bryant & May's	£40
Cadbury's	£40-£60
Campbell's Soups, Wiedersheim	£35
Camp Coffee, Harry Payne	£50
others	£35
Continental Tyres	£20-£35
C.W.S.	£10-£25
Fry's	£20-£50
Tom Browne designs	£15-£35
Gossage's Soap	£30
Holbrooks Ltd.	£20
Horniman's Tea	£20-£25
H.M. & Co's Famous Posters	£30-£40
Keiller, James	£15
Nestles Milk	£25-£40
North British Rubber Co.	£30
Ogdens	£80
Peak Frean's, Tom Browne	£15-£20
Players	£60
St Ivel Cheese, court size	£12
Shell *(beware of modern reprints)*	£30-£45
Skipper Sardines	£10
Tuck's Celebrated Posters	
Dewar's, Cadbury's	£15
other designs	£30-£60
later series and rare cards	£70-£120
French series	£80
Viscan Pet Foods	£10
Wills	£80
Wood Milne Rubber Heels	£10-£25
Overseas tobacco companies	£10-£40
Other products	£10+

Artists

Browne, Tom	£15-£125
Hassall, John	£25-£35
Martini, L.B.	£20-£45
Payne, G.M.	£8
Payne, Harry	£35-£150
Wiedersheim, G.G.	£35

NON-POSTER ADVERTS

Cards distributed by manufacturers as publicity matter, representatives' cards, order confirmation etc. Some bear no relation to the product. There are many inexpensive cards in this category. Below will be found some of the better ones.

Bovril, paintings	75p
Broma Cocoa, plantation sketches	£2
Cadbury's, butterflies	£8
Bourneville views	£3+
Canadian Dept. of Emigration	£2.50-£4
Capern's Bird Food, birds	£3
Carter's Seeds	£1-£2
Chivers & Sons, fruit	£1.50
Clay Cross Co. mining	£12
Colman's Starch	£8
Cook, E., aviation	£6
C.W.S. 'Time Around the World'	£10
De Beukelaer's Cocoa, etc.	75p
De Beukelaer's, cats	£8
Elliman's Linament, Tuck	£3
Epps Cocoa, nature series	£6
Fitzall Bandeau Co., fashions	£5
Formosa Oolong Tea	
on rice paper	£8-£15
Fry's	£5
G.P. Govt. Tea, composite	£120
Glaxo	£1
Godfrey Philips	£2
Goss, W.H. nos 1-6	£8
nos 7&8	£10
Grays Cigarettes	£3
Guinness	£8
production scenes	£3-£6
Heinz	£12-£15
Hoffmans Starch	£3-£10

With nice military interest. £45

STONECHAT

ISSUED BY CADBURY, BOURNVILLE

A Cadbury reward card. £4

REWARD CARD

Presented to ....

STONECHAT

THE Stonechat is a bold, restless bird, continually flitting from one point to another, and its song is short but sweet. Its food is chiefly insects, though in winter it eats worms. It rarely goes far out of the bushes in search of a meal. A neat nest of dry grass and moss is generally concealed at the bottom of a furze bush, and in it are laid, at the beginning of May, from four to six pale bluish-green eggs marked with faint red spots.

BOURNVILLE COCOA

Whilst you are enjoying its delicious flavour remember that it is food too, which keeps you fit and helps you to study better and enjoy your games more.

See the name Cadbury on every piece of chocolate.

The back of the same card.

Horniman's Tea, views	£2
invisible picture	£4
International Horse Show	£4-£10
King Insurance Co.	
kings & queens	£6
Lemco, Coronation	£15
cattle	£8
Lever Bros., Port Sunlight	75p-£1.50
Lipton Tea	£2
Liverpool, China & India Tea Co. Ltd.	
Atlantic liners	£6
Mazawattee Tea & Chocolate	
Louis Wain cats, trade back	£30
Louis Wain cats, postcard	£35
Mellin's Food	£4-£8
Molassine Meal	£8
Nestles	£2+
New Departure Coaster Hub,	
G.M. Payne	£8
Nicholas Sarony	£2
North British Rubber Co., golf	£15
Ocean Accident Corp.	£2
Odd Fellows Friendly Society	£4+
Odol Dentifrice, actresses	£2
Oxo	£4
Peak Frean's, invisible picture	£6
Philips	£5-£15
Phoenix, poultry/dog foods	£8
Pickfords, transport art types	£6
Pitman Health Food Co.	£1
Players	£10-£20
Price's Candles, battle scenes	£6
Price's Candles, nursery riddles	£8
Quaker Oat smiles	£8
R.&J. Lea Chairman's series	£5
with suppliers imprint	£6
Reckitts, naval	£6
Ridgway's Tea	£1.50
Rowntree	£1+
Sainsbury, J. Pure Tea,	
fairy tales	£4
Selfridge Co.	£2-£4
Singer Sewing Machines	
aircraft	£4
battleships	£3
sewing machines worldwide	£6
Spillers	£8
Sportex Cloth, dogs	£6
Spratt's Dog Food	£6-£8

Steedman's Powders	£6
Suchard Chocolate, vignettes	£25
Sutton & Sons	£2
Tower Tea, proverbs series	£8
Trent Pottery	£4
Ty-Phoo Tea, Oilette type	
views & animals	£1.50+
Viscan	£10
Airlines	£2-£6
Department stores	£2-£4
Overseas tobacco companies	£1.50-£2.50

MAGAZINE INSERTS
Given away with newspapers and magazines.

Captain Magazine, Tom Browne	£6
Girls' Own Paper	£4-£8
'Ideas' Weekly, The Imps	£6
Pearson's Weekly "Germs"	£4
T.A.T.	£2+
Weekly Telegraph, Tom Browne	£6
Weldon's Bazaar	£2.50
Coronation souvenir 1902	£8

Most other inserts are still readily obtainable at prices from 25p-£1.

REWARD POSTCARDS
Given away by education committees, school boards, Sunday schools etc. as 'reward' for regular and/or punctual attendence. Many bear the legend 'never absent, never late'.

Cadbury's, birds/eggs	£6
Cadbury's, butterflies	£8
Cadbury's, map cards	£6
Milkmaid Milk	£5
Nectar Tea	£5
Reckitt & Sons,	
heroes & heroines	£4
Scott's Emulsion	£4
Others	£1+

The Poultry Yard from Tuck set 9464. £4

A better R.J. Wealthy for Tuck. £4

Cats have gone through the roof, and are avidly collected all over Europe. Certain breeds of dogs are sought as are pigs, chickens, butterflies and frogs, with Louis Wain and Thiele vying to be the most expensive artist.

GENERAL

Birds	£1.50-£3
Bulldogs	£2.50-£6
Butterflies	£3-£8
Cats, coloured	£1-£6
b&w	50p-£1
Cattle	50p-£2
Dogs, coloured	£1.50-£3
b&w	75p-£3
art types	£2-£4
Donkeys	75p-£2.50
working	£3-£12
Dressed animals,	
anthropomorphics	£1.50-£4
Horses	75p-£2.50
working	£2-£8
Hunting art	£3-£8
photographic,	
named locations	£4-£8
Tuck's Oilettes	£2.50-£3.50
Poultry	£1.50-£4
Tortoises and turtles	£2-£4
Welfare societies	£3-£8
Wild animals, b&w	50p-£1
coloured	£1-£2
Landons studies	75p
Zoo animals	£1-£2
official cards	£1.50-£2.50
Tuck educational series	£8

ARTISTS

Ackroyd, W.M.	£1.50
Ainsley, Anne	£1
Aldin, Cecil	£4-£6
Ambler, C.	£1
Anders, O.	£3-£5
Austin, E.H.S. Barnes	£8
Austin, Winifred (birds)	£3
Barnes, A.E.	£15
Barnes, G.L.	£4
Bebb, Rosa	£5
Beraud, N.	£2-£4
Billinge, Ophelia	£2-£4
Boulanger, Maurice	£10-£15
Calland, H.J.	£3-£5
Chatterton, F.J.S.	£5
Cobbe, B.	£2-£3
Daws, F.T.	£4
Donaldini, Jr.	£2-£4
Drummond, Eileen	£2-£3
Drummond, Norah	£4-£6
Gear, M.	£2-£3
Green, Roland	£2.50-£4
Hayes, Sidney	£1.50-£2.50
Hood, Eileen	£2-£4
Hunt, Edgar	£1.50
Hunt, Muriel	£2-£4
Hunter, Mildred C.	£2-£4
Kaufmann, J.C.	£1.50
Keene, Minnie	£2-£3
Kennedy, A.E.	£3-£5
Kirmse, Persis	£3-£5
Klein, Christina	£2.50
Lester, Adrienne	£1
Mac	£4-£6
Maguire, Helena	£4-£10
Merte, O.	£2-£4
Mills, Ernest H.	£3
Mutter, K.	£3
Nielsen, Vivienne	£1.50
Parker, N.	£2-£3
Payne, Harry, early	£25+
Oilette	£6
Perlberg, F.	£2-£4
Pope, Dorothy T.	£4-£8
Rankin, George	£2.50
Reichert, C.	£3-£5
Roberts, Violet	£20
Rowntree, Harry	£8+
Scrivener, Maude	£2.50
Shaw, H.G.	£4
Sperlich, T.	£6-£10
Stokes, G. Vernon	£1.50
Stretton, Philip	£2-£4
Talboys, A.	£1.50
Thiele, Arthur	£15-£30

ANIMALS

Thorne, Diana	75p
Valter, Eugenie M.	£3
Valter, Florence E.	£3
Wain, Louis	
advertising	£30-£60
later issues	£25-£35
Oilette	£30+
vignette, unused	£30-£40
vignette, written on front	£15-£20
Walker, Hilda	£3
Wardle, Arthur	£3.50
Watson, C.M. West	£3.50
Wealthy, R.J.	£1.50
West, A.L.	£1
Wright, Gilbert	75p+

The largest of all land animals. £4

*See also Comic. Animals are also found on
most types of Greetings cards and on some
Novelty cards. For product advertising, see
Advertising. A full listing of Harry Payne
series is given under Artists.*

Fox Terriers. Sent through the post in 1903. £8

An important postcard classification. At its peak Art Deco reached into almost every aspect of graphic and domestic design. It was particularly memorable in the Hollywood film sets of the 1930s and in the geometrical lines of contemporary architecture and ceramics. Designs are noticeable for their bold use of colour and exaggeration of style.

Anichini, Ezio	£8	Katinka	£8
Birger	£15	Koehler, Mela	£30-£60
Brunelleschi	£80-£100	Koehler, Mela Broman	£8-£15
Busi, Adolfo	£8-£10	Longley, Chilton	£20
Chilton, G.	£15	Loreley	£10
Chiostri	£10-£30	Marty, Andre	£8-£15
Corbella, Tito	£10-£15	Mauzan, A.	£10-£15
Cowderoy, K.E.	£10-£15	Mercer, Joyce	£15-£20
Cramer, Rie	£12-£15	Meschini, G.	£25
Gobbis, D.	£15	Montedoro, M.	£30-£45
Graf, Marte	£6	Nerman	£10-£15
Grosze, Manni	£6	Rylander	£10-£12
Grunewald	£6	Shand, C.E.	£10-£12
Harbour, Jennie	£10	Stenberg, Aina	£8
Hardy, F.	£6	Tanquerey L.	£4

CONFIDENZE AMOROSE

Pure Art Deco by Meschini. £25

C.T. Howard hedgehogs published by water colour specialists, Salmon. £2.50

Many postcard artists produced work which can be assigned to one category. For example, A.R. Quinton was exclusively a topographical artist, while Louis Wain was primarily a cat artist, although he also drew other animals. Such artists who concentrated on one or two subject areas can be found under the appropriate subject heading.

However, some artists worked across many genres. These artists defy any meaningful classification or categorisation, and are listed below, together with an up-to-date listing of some of the work of Harry Payne, one of the foremost, most versatile, and best collected of postcard artists.

Beecroft, Herbert	£4	Prosnocimi, A.	£6-£8
Coppola, A.	£6	Ritter, Paul	£4
Gardener, E.C. (ECG)	£1-£3	Salaman, Edith	£5
Guggenberger, T.	£10	Sauber	£4-£6
Hey, Paul	£2-£6	Schubert, H.	£3
Howard, C.T.	£1-£3	Schweiger, L.	£4
Lilien, E.M.	£8	Spindler	£6
Lynnen, Amedee	£4	Utrillo, A.	£5
Muller, Valery	£8	Voellmy, F.	£6-£8
Pfaff, C.	£6	Wishaw, M.C. (MCW)	£2+
Reiss, Fritz	£4		

Harry Payne from Stewart and Woolf series 436. £12

ARTISTS: HARRY PAYNE

We are very pleased to present this updated version of part of the Harry Payne supplement, first published in the 1981 Picton's catalogue. This is a precis of a larger work prepared by the late Mr.E.H.Cooper, M.A.(Cantab.), who, before he died, kindly agreed to allow us to re-publish it in order to bring it up to date. In this edition of the RF Price Guide we have included a complete and up-to-date listing of the Harry Payne military cards, plus information on some previously unattributed 'miscellaneous' cards. Full details of the other miscellaneous cards, as well as the rural and advertising listings, will appear in future editions of this price guide.

In his original manuscript Mr.Cooper made grateful acknowledgements as follows, 'for the help and encouragement [I have received]; from Michael Cane; from Jack Duke who has given freely of his time and knowledge; from Tony Byatt for his help and advice which we readily endorse and to which we add; Tony Warr for information he has provided on the Tuck 'Empire' Series' 1424 and 1425.

Biography

Harry Payne was born at Newington on 8th March 1868 to Joseph and Margaret Payne. There was no history of artistic talent in the family, but from an early age, both Harry and his brother Arthur displayed considerable creative ability.

The only formal art instruction that Harry received was a few months of evening classes at art school. Nonetheless, after spending two years in a merchant's office, he managed to secure the post of art designer to a firm of army and navy clothing contractors, and it was here that he developed the meticulous attention to detail that he later became famous for.

Harry continued to produce illustrations and paintings in his spare time and these came to the attention of Lionel Marks, a well known London dealer. As a result of the ensuing friendship between the men, Harry gave up his job to concentrate full time on painting at the age of 21, effectively being sponsored by Marks.

In 1882 Harry and his brother Arthur chanced to see the Hampshire Yeomanry on manoeuvres near Portsmouth. Impressed by this splendid sight, Payne was moved to join the West Kent (Queen's Own) Yeomanry in the following year, 1883, and became firmly determined to make military art his career.

Harry Payne's thirty-six year association with Raphael Tuck began in 1884. Commissions were plentiful, not only for book illustrations, regimental histories, and scraps for sticking in scrapbooks, but also for privately requested oil paintings.

Harry married in 1897, moving to Catford with his wife Teresa six years later. Around this time the 'postcard era' began and he produced his first designs for court cards, both for Tuck and M.H. Nathan and Co. Following his retirement from the West Kent Yeomanry in 1906, Payne's happiest and most prolific period as an artist began. The following twelve years saw a prodigious output of highly sophisticated postcard designs, all deeply researched to ensure that his military subject matter was depicted with complete accuracy.

Meanwhile, Harry's brother Arthur had specialised in architectural paintings, producing a series of designs on English cathedrals for Tuck. He was thus well equipped to collaborate with Harry in the production of the 'Military in London' series (Tuck 9081 and 6412), providing the architectural backdrops for his brother's military studies.

During this period Harry also illustrated a number of Tuck's 'toy' books. Many of these illustrations were subsequently produced as postcards, the most famous being number 9877, 'King George V'. He also designed a delightful series of twenty-four cards for Stewart and Woolf.

1918 saw both the end of the war and the end of the postcard boom. At sixty years of age Harry Payne's arrangement with Raphael Tuck came to an end, although during 1918 he was commissioned by Gale and Polden to paint a new series of postcards. These were completed in 1919, but only around twenty of the original 67 were issued, and these cards, along with a couple of others designed for Gale and Polden, were probably his last work.

Over the next few years, commissions were few and far between. Payne's health was not particularly good, and in 1927 he died of influenza, aged 69. His place of burial is not known. Teresa, his wife, outlived him by many years, dying in 1953 at the great age of 92, and there is a delightful portrait of her and Harry's dog Jock coming through a gate in Tuck 9550, 'Spring Blossoms - the laburnum'. A self-portrait of Harry can be found in Tuck's 'British Army' Series 19, card number 108 entitled 'Royal Horse Guards' . This is repeated in larger format in set 6088 'On Service'.

The total number of Harry Payne's designs issued as postcards - so far as can be ascertained - was between 556 and 560. This total excludes any of the cards that Richard Carline suggests that Harry designed (unsuccessfully) for Tuck's 'Amewsing Write-Away' series There is no evidence that Harry ever drew a cat in his life!

THE MILITARY POSTCARDS

Harry Payne is, without question, the best known of the military postcard artists. His meticulous attention to detail and his excellent treatment of the horse make his cards a pleasure to view. However, Harry Payne cards vary considerably in quality. Early examples in both the Tuck British Army and Stewart & Woolf series are particularly fine, while later cards published by Gale & Polden have a curiously lifeless quality.

Raphael Tuck & Sons
Considerable confusion exists in many collectors' minds regarding the number of Harry Payne military cards and sets issued by Tuck. However, it should be borne in mind that Tuck's were in the business of selling postcards, and they did not hesitate to issue 'new' sets made up of previously published cards. Typical examples of made-up sets are Series 3642 'Scots Pipers', and Series 3546 'Military in London'. Similarly, the early cards 100-133 were made up into nine groups of six to form sets 18-27. As there were only 34 different designs in total, there is some duplication in these sets.

ARTISTS: HARRY PAYNE

18, The British Navy £25
These superb chromo-litho cards were issued in 1900-01. They are horizontal vignettes with undivided backs. Some are very rare, and all are difficult to obtain in good condition. See also Series 6087.
Bound for Shore *100*
Letters from Home *101*
On the Look-out *102*
Writing Home *103*
Far Away *104*
Topmen Aloft *105*

19-26, The British Army £25
Card 118 is unsigned although obviously by Payne as it was previously issued as a court card (as were many others in this series). Numbers 122, 123 & 124 are by Arthur Payne.
Royal Highlanders - The Black Watch *106*
11th Hussars - Prince Albert's Own *107*
Royal Horse Guards *108*
The 17th Lancers - Duke of
    Cambridge's Own *109*
The 93rd Highlanders *110*
Grenadier Guards - Guardsman *111*
The 7th Hussars *112*
The 17th Lancers *113*
Gordon Highlanders - Band *114*
11th Hussars - Band *115*
Coldstream Guards - Band *116*
Royal Horse Guards - Band (Blues) *117*
Gordon Highlanders - Private *118*
Infantry of the Line - Private *119*
5th Lancers (Royal Irish) *120*
2nd Dragoons (Royal Scots Greys) *121*
Cheering Effects of the National Music[1] *122*
Heavy Cavalry - lightly handled[1] *123*
Light Cavalry - Mounting the Major[1] *124*
Royal Irish Lancers *125*
2nd Dragoon Guards - Off Duty *126*
10th Hussars - Prince of Wales' Own *127*
Royal Horse Guards - Trumpeter *128*
Coldstream Guards - Drummer Boy *129*
Argyll and Sutherland Highlanders - Fifer[2] *130*
12th Lancers - The Scout *131*
15th Hussars - Charge *132*
2nd Dragoon Guards *133*
1 These three cards are by Arthur Payne

2 Card 130 can be found overprinted as a greetings card from Scotland, with a quotation from Burns, and a sprig of real heather stuck to it. Extremely rare.

27, The Empire Series £15-£25
Sepia vignettes with undivided backs.
Something Off the Slate[1] *280*
Baden-Powell[1] *281*
Sons of the Empire *1280*
Sons of the Empire[2] *1282*
1 27 probably consisted of these two cards only triplicated.
2 8761 'Defenders of the Empire' was based on this card.

6087, For England, Home & Beauty £35
Full-sized editions of the 'British Navy' Series cards #100-105. As they were seldom sent through the post, but mounted as pictures or stuck in scrap books they are very rare indeed.
Bound for the Shore
Letters from Home
On the Lookout
Writing Home
Far Away
Topmen Aloft

6088, On Service £35
Based on the 'British Army Series' #s 106, 107, 108, 109, 111 and 113.
11th Hussars
Royal Horse Guards
The 17th Lancers (full length)
Grenadier Guards - Guardsmen
The 17th Lancers (head)
Royal Highlanders

8085, Christmas £45
As above but very rare indeed.
Dismounted trooper of 1st Life Guards with
    horse being decorated with
    holly by a girl.[1]
Trooper 11th Hussars standing on horse's
    saddle gathering Mistletoe.[1]
Mounted and dismounted Troopers 16th
    Lancers bringing in the holly.
1 These cards were previously issued by Tuck as court cards. Other cards in set may be 11th Hussars, 1st Dragoons and Royal Horse Guards.

8738, Types of the British Army £25
This fine set is superior to the usual run of Oilettes and are more like chromo-lithos.

Payne's signature is difficult to find on some cards. The designs are 'composed' from early paintings used for purposes other than postcards. Some of the horses' heads in these designs are used for the rare cards #550 and 555 in Series 94, British Chargers, and card 549, Series 93, Animal Life.
Royal Horse Guards
17th Lancers and 1st King's Dragoon Guards
3rd Dragoon Guards
Royal Scots Greys and 13th Hussars
11th Hussars
12th Lancers

THE OILETTE SERIES

3100, Cavalry on Active Service £15-£20
Lancers attacking Infantry
Across the Enemy's Trenches
Bringing in Prisoners, Egypt, 1917
Charge, Battle of the Somme
Charge at St. Quentin
Hussars Skirmishing on Western Front, 1917

3105, Our Fighting Regiments -
The Royal Artillery £8-£10
Modern reproductions exist of this set.
Field Day - 1717
Battle of Plassey - 1757
Battle of Waterloo - 1815
Crimenan War - 1854-5
South African War - 1899-1902
Battle of the Marne - 1914

3113, Comrades £20
Standing by his Wounded Master
His Wounded Chum
Fetching his Chum Some Water
A Kindly Lead
A Drink for his Pal
Giving him a Tit-bit

3159, The U.S. Army
on the Western Front £25
Regimental Colours and Escort
Over the Top
On the March through Flanders
In the Trenches
With Bomb and Bayonet

Cold Steel

3163, Our Fighting Regiments:
1st Life Guards £15
Coronation King Charles II - 1660
Dettingen - 1743
Waterloo - 1815
Kassassin - 1882
South Africa - 1899-1902
Klein Zille Beke - 1914

3165, Our Fighting Regiments:
1st Dragoon Guards £15
King James II Reviewing - 1685
Dettingen - 1743
Cateau - 1794
Waterloo - 1815
South Africa - 1902
Great War - Spring 1917
Modern reproductions of the above set exist.

8625, The Scots Guards £6
Officers Visiting Patrol
The King's Guard
The Relief
Field-day in Drill Order
The Regimental Marching to a State
Ceremonial
Piper

8635, The 21st Lancers £6
Attention
Waiting the Order to Mount
Getting out a Stone from the Foot
Officer, Trumpeter and Squadron,
Review Order
Scouting
Drums and Band

8637, 17th Lancers £6
The Drums and Band
Mount
The Advance Guard
Going on Escort Duty
Telling Off for Road Duty
A Charge for the Hill

8731, Our Territorials £15
Ready to a Man

ARTISTS: HARRY PAYNE

Off to the Front
These may be the only cards by Payne in the series as no specimens of the last four cards, if they exist, have yet been found.

8761, Defenders of the Empire £6
A Group Depicting all Three Services.
Based on a redrawn version of Card 1282. Also known with the embossed overprint 'Victory' and worth £8. On later copies the dates 1915-1916 are omitted from the front of the cards.

8762, The Red Cross Series £25
Wounded from Red Cross Ship
Wounded Seaman
Wounded Soldier
Two Nurses and Wounded Soldier
Two Orderlies and Wounded Soldier
How He Won the Victoria Cross - Admiral Raby. *Not by Payne.*

8763, Royal Horse Artillery £8
Officer and Trumpeter
The Drums
In Action
On the March
In Full Gallop
Across Country

8807, 16th Lancers £12
In Review Order
Inspecting Officer's Orderly
Scouting
A Despatch from the Front
Charge
In the Thick of It

8831, 1st (Royal) Dragoons £15
The Regiment in Review Order
The Drums and Band
A Patrol Reconnoitring
Charge
A Message from the Front
Fording a River under Shell-fire

8835, 1st Life Guards £12-£15
The Band and Drums
On Royal Escort
Officers Patrol
A Scout

On King's Guard
At Close Quarters

8848, 11th Hussars (Cherry Pickers) £12
Escort Duty
The Regiment in Line
The Drums and Band
A Surprise Attack
Reconnoitring
Somewhere in France

8890, 6th Dragoon Guards £12
The Drums and Band
The Regiments in Review Order
Scouting in the Early Morning
A Dangerous Path
A Patrol Reconnoitring
A Charge up the Hill

9081, Military in London II £4
Royal Horse Artillery
Horse Guards - Parade
Royal Horse Guards
21st Lancers - Orderlies
Grenadier Guards
Coldstream Guards - Bank Guard

9139, Military Life & Military Tournaments £5
7th Dragoon Guards - Water Jump
16th Lancers - Tent Pegging
14th Hussars - V.C. Race
10th Hussars - Lemon Cutting
Sword v Sword
Lance v Bayonet

9527, Life at Aldershot £12-£15
Infantry Skirmishing
Red Coats and Pink Heather
21st Lancers - Cleaning Kit
Royal Horse Artillery - Stables
Going to the Review
5th Lancers - Sentry

9587, Military in London III £4

7th Hussars - Road Duty
Changing Guard - Buckingham Palace
Gordon Highlanders

Irish Guards - Band
State Opening of Parliament
King's Guard - Whitehall

9883, Queens Own
 Cameron Highlanders £6
Field Officer and Drummer - Review Order
The Colours
Drummer, Bandsman and Piper
Company Officer, Drill Order
Mounting Guard
A Charge Up the Hill

9884, Gordon Highlanders £6
Sergeant Bandsman and Drummer
The King's Colours
Piper
After the Review
Swarming Down the Hill
Field Officer, Company Officer

9885, Seaforth Highlanders £8
Officer - Drill Order and Sentry
Sergeant and Two Privates
The Colours
Marching to the Review
Piper and Bandsman
Repelling an Attack

9934, For Home and Empire £15-£25
What are you doing to Guard the
 Homes of England?[1]
Before Joining the Territorials and After
Boy Scouts - Good Use of Holiday Hours
1 Same card as 8732. There may only be three cards in this
set as no other cards have turned up yet.

9937, Argyll and Sutherland
 Highlanders £6
Returning from the Review
Officers - Review and Mess Uniforms
Piper
Drill Instruction
Company - Marching Order
Patrol - Reconnoitring

9980, Royal Scots Greys £6
Trumpeters - Review Order
Officer - Review Order

Sentry - Review Order
Trooper - File Out
Drums and Band
In Khaki Drill Order

9993, Coldstream Guards £6
The Band
Drummer
Sentry
Changing Guard - St. James's
Field Officer - Review Order
Parade - Drill Order

9994, Black Watch £5
Relieving Sentries
The Colonel's Inspection
Piper - Review Order
Field & Company Officers
Sergeant and Bandsmen

*Series 9993, 9884, 9081, 9587 and the 'made
up' set 6412 were sold at the British Empire
Exhibition. Some of these cards may not be by
Harry or Arthur Payne.*

**REGIMENTAL BADGES AND THEIR
WEARER SERIES**
*These five series were issued between 1913 and
1917. The faces of the 'wearers' are curiously
wooden but the badges are exquisite. 3204
and 3205 are very rare and the South African
card of 3160 is hard to come by.*

3160, Colonial Badges
 and their Wearers £8-£10
Canada - Cavalry
Canada - Infantry
New Zealand - Infantry
Australia - Infantry
South Africa - Infantry
Newfoundland - Infantry

3204, Badges and their Wearers £75
The Royal Horse Guards
2nd Dragoons
6th Dragoon Guards
2nd Dragoons
16th Lancers - Queen's
15th Hussars - Kings

ARTISTS: HARRY PAYNE

3205, Badges and their Wearers £75
The Royal Fusiliers
The Middlesex Regiment
19th Hussars
The Grenadier Guards
9th Lancers
The Royal Marines

8491, Badges and their Wearers £50
The Army Medical Corps
The Seaforth Highlanders
The Army Ordnance Corps
The Army Service Corps
Royal Flying Corps - Pilot
The Royal Engineers

8871, Badges and their Wearers £10
10th Royal Hussars
Coldstream Guards
King's Royal Rifle Corps
Gordon Highlanders
17th Lancers
The Royal Artillery

THE 'MADE UP' SETS

3546, Military in London £4
Made up from 9081 and 9587

3642, Scots Pipers £4
Made up from 8625, 9883, 9884, 9885, 9937
and 9994

6412, Military in London £4
Changing Guard[1]
Mounting Guard[1]
March Past[2]
Pipers[2]
2nd Life Guards[2]
Scots Guards[3]
1 By Harry and Arthur Payne
2 Not by Harry Payne
3 Same card is in 8625

8732, Wake up England £15
Same Card as in 9934

8770, Regimental Bands £4-£5
*Made up from bands depicted in 'The Military
in London' and other series and priced the
same*

9762, Scotch Pipers £5-£8
Made up from 9884, 9885, 9937 and 9994

Gale and Polden Series
*Apart from the meticulous attention to detail in
the uniforms, these cards have little to
commend them. They were commissioned in
1919 and were probably used as recruiting
cards, as well as being for sale in the canteens
of the relevant regiments. Although Payne
produced 67 paintings for these cards only
about twenty-four were actually issued. They
may not have proved very popular and it is
unlikely, in view of their probable use, that
they were packaged in sets of six. Some cards
are difficult to come by.*

**All cards are price at £12 except for
numbers 2128 and 2131 which are £20 each.**

Scots Guards *2126*
Norfolk Regiment *2127*
Devonshire Regiment *2128*
Suffolk Regiment *2129*
Leicestershire Regiment *2130*
Somerset Light Infantry *2131*
Royal Irish Regiment *2132*
Royal Scots Fusiliers[1] *2133*
King's Own Scottish Borderers *2134*
Royal Inniskilling Fusiliers *2135*
Duke of Cornwall's Light Infantry *2136*
Duke of Wellington's Regiment *2137*
Border Regiment *2138*
Loyal North Lancashire Regiment *2139*
King's Own Yorkshire Light Infantry *2140*
North Staffordshire Regiment *2141*
[2]*2142*
[2]*2143*
Gordon Highlanders *2150*
Middlesex Regiment *2151*
Royal Welsh Fusiliers *2152*
Rifle Brigade *2153*
Royal Fusiliers (City of London Regt.) *2154*
South Wales Borderers *2155*

Albuhera 16th May 1811[3]
Minden 1st August 1759[3]
1 Cards with a plain back, no number and no title, issued by
Gale and Polden, are proofs.
2 May not have been issued.
3 Unnumbered and very rare.

Stewart and Woolf Series
*This delightful series was probably issued in
1906-7. The dates which appear on some
cards refer to the period the uniform was worn
in, and not the date of issue. Certain cards are
very hard to come by.*

436, No title £12
Infantry Sergeant
Officer - Rifle Brigade, 1905
Piper - Scots Guards, 1905
Private - Argyll and Sutherland Highlanders,
1904
Grenadier Guardsman
Officer, R.A.M.C. Officer wears a sword -
      presumably for quick amputations in
      the field!

437, No title £12
2nd Dragoon Guards
3rd Dragoon Guards
14th Hussars
21st Lancers
Royal Horse Artillery
Royal Horse Guards

505, No title £12
6th Dragoon Guards
5th Royal Irish Lancers
18th Hussars
1st Life Guards
1st King's Dragoon Guards
Mounted Infantry

506, No title £12
10th Hussars
16th Lancers
Royal Field Artillery
Royal Engineers
Rifle Brigade
1st King's Dragoon Guards
*Series 505 and 506 are also found published
by H.& S. (Holland).*

A.M. Davis and Company
War Bond Campaign postcards, £6.
*Only one card (Design 12: 60 Pounder Moving
up in Support) in the set is by Payne and it isn't
signed.*

SECTION 2:
TUCK MISCELLANEOUS SERIES

38A, 'Sport' Series - Hunting £20
*These superb chromo-litho cards, printed in
Saxony, are horizontal half-size vignettes with
undivided backs, dated from 1900-01. Rare.*
A Fair Leader *187*
The Last Fence *188*
In the Hunt *189*
Barred! *190*
First Over the Fence *191*
Out of the Hunt *192*

39B, Coaching £25
*As in 38A above. Four cards only with two
duplicates.*
Meeting of Coaching Club *193*
A Good Team. The Start *194*
Through the Park -
      Meet of Four in Hand Club *195*
A Capital Turnout *196*

1424 £25
**1425, In the Highlands with Prince
      Albert and John Brown £25**

*Both sets 1424 and 1425 are part of the Tuck
Empire series. They are sepia or b&w vignette
scenes from the life of Queen Victoria, taken
from scraps by Harry and Arthur Payne to
commemorate her Jubilee.*

ART NOUVEAU

'Adolescence'. Originally used as an advert for Chocolat Masson. £185

It's still possible to collect Art Nouveau on the cheap. Only £4

Well collected in Europe and the USA, by Raphael Kirchner. £65

A style of decorative art, characterised by curving, sinuous lines, which flourished particularly in books and poster design, during the last 20 years or so of the 19th century. By the time the postcard reached its peak, the movement was almost over, although Klimt & Hoffman founded the Viennese Secession (Weiner Werkstatte) in 1897 which flourished well into the 20th century and merged into the Art Deco period of the 1920s and 30s. *Where a range of price is given for artists in this section the higher price usually applies to cards from one of the major 'collections'.*

ARTISTS

Abeille, Jack	£30-£35
Bakst, Leon	£35
Basch, Arpad	£100-£130
Berthon, P.	£80-£100
Bilibin	£25-£35
Boutet, H.	£20
Cauvy, Leon	£30
Cheret, Jules	£50-£120
Christiansen, Hans	£100-£150
Combaz, Gisbert	£100
proverbs	£75
Daniell, Eva	£75
Docker, E. Jnr.	£40
Feure de	£150-£250
Fidus, H.A. von	£50
French, Annie	£75
Grasset, Eugene	£80
Hager, Nini	£50
Hampel, Walter	£40-£80
Hart, Josef	£25
Hoffmann, J.	£60-£120
Hohenstein, A.	£20-£30
Jossot	£100-£200
Jozsa, C.	£40
Jung, Maurice	£600
Kainradl, L.	£75-£150
King, Jessie M.	£75
Kirchner, Raphael, early	£50-£100
Koehler, Mela	£80-£200
Konopa	£30
Kosa	£125
Kokoschka, Oscar	£600-£800
Kulas, J.V.	£30
Kupka	£60
Larcombe, Ethel	£25
Lautrec, Henri de Toulouse	£500-£750
Laskoff, F.	£40
Lelee, Leopold	£20-£85
Lessieux, E.L.	£30-£40
Livremont, Privat	£125
Loffler, Berthold	£80-£150
Loffler, Lovat	£25
MacDonald, A.K.	£25+
Marisch	£25-£100
Mataloni, G.	£20
Metlicovitz, L.	£20-£30
Meunier, Henri	£70-£100
Mignot, Victor	£30
Moser, Koloman	£100-£150
Mucha, Alphonse	£175-£300
Slav period	£40-£50
Noury, Gaston	£30-£75
Ost, A.	£15-£25
Patella, B.	£30
Pinkawa, A.	£25
Popini	£25
Rossi, J.C.	£30-£50
Schiele, Egon	£100-£1500
Smale, B.H.	£5
Smith, Jessie Wilcox	£15
Sonrel, Elisabeth	£40
Steinlen, Alexandre	£60-£100
Turrian, E.D.	£20
Villon, Jacques	£300-£400
Wanke, Alice	£15-£20
Wennerberg, Brynolf	£10-£20

Those toys are worth a small fortune now. £8

MY! YOU ARE FRECKLED!

Flora White giraffe. £4

"His socks."   "Ses chaussettes."

From Inter Art 'Fairies' series. £5

These cards are widely collected in Western Europe and America, Britain being one of the chief sources of supply. Because of currency values our prices are very cheap compared with other countries. Demand for teddies and Florence Upton gollies continues unabated.

GENERAL

Alice in Wonderland	£4-£10
'Coons'	£3-£8
Dolls, photographic	£3-£6
Elves/fairies	£4-£6
Golliwogs	£2-£5
Mirror Grange	£2.50
Nursery rhymes	£2-£5
Posed photographic studies	£1-£1.50
Queen's dolls house	£2.50
Wembley exhibition	£3
Social history type	£2-£6
School groups, identified	£4-£6
Teddy bears	
photographic	£3-£6
art	£4-£20
pull-outs, etc.	£5
Roosevelt cartoons	£15+
Titania's Palace	£1.50
Toys, close up	£3-£6

ARTISTS

Alys, M.	£1
Anderson, Anne	£5
Attwell, Mabel Lucie	
early	£6
middle period	£5
later	£4
modern	20p-40p
Azzoni	£1
Barber, C.W.	£2
Barham, S.	£6
Barker, Cicely M. (CMB)	£6
Barribal, W.	£6
Bertiglia, A.	£3-£5
Birch, Nora Annie	£2
Boriss, Margret	£4
Bowden, Doris	£3-£4
Bowley, A.L.	£8-£12
Brett, Molly	£2-£3
Brisley, Nora	£2
Brundage, Frances	
chromo-litho	£12

others	£3-£5
Butcher, Arthur	£2.50
Caldecott, Randolph	£1.50
Clapsaddle, E.H.	£4-£6
Cloke, Rene	£5-£6
Coleman, W.S.	£3-£6
Colombo, E.	£3
Cooper, Phyllis, early	£6-£8
later	£2
Cottom, C.M.	£2+
Cowderoy, K.E.	£4-£6
Cowham, Hilda	£3-£6
Cramer, Rie	£10-£15
Dawson, Muriel	£5
Dexter, Marjorie	£2
Dinah	£2-£3
Drayton, G.	£6-£8
Duddle, Josephine	£5
Duncan, J. Ellen	75p
Ebner, Pauli	£6
Edgerton, Linda	£4
Feiertag, K.	£1-£3
Folkard, Charles	£10-£12
Forres, Kit	50p
Fradkin, E.	50p
Gassaway, Katherine	£4
Gibbs, May	£30
Goethen, Evan	£5
Goodman, Maud	
chromo-litho	£15
Hildersheimer	£1
Govey, Lilian	£4-£6
Greenaway, Kate, 1903 printing	£50
Greiner, M.	£6
Grey, Mollie	50p
Hansi	£12-£15
Hardy, Florence	£4-£8
Hartridge, Norman	£6
Henry, Thomas	£3
Hollyer, Eva	£4-£6
Jackson, Helen	£12-£15
Jacobs, Helen	£5
James, Ivy Millicent (IMJ)	£3-£5
Kaskeline, Fred	£4
Kempe	£3

CHILDREN

Kidd, Will	£3	Tempest, Margaret	£2-£4
Kinsella, E.P.	£5-£15	Twelvetrees, C.H.	£2-£3
Lambert, H.G.C. Marsh	£4	Upton, Florence K., unused	£20
Lewin, F.G.	£4-£6	used	£15+
Lowe, Meta	75p	Wanke, Alice	£5
Ludovici, A.	£4	Wheeler, Dorothy	£1
Mair, H. Willebeek Le	£6-£8	White, Brian	£2
Mallet, Beatrice	£3	White, Flora	£4-£5
Margetson, Hester	£5	Wichera, R.R.	£5+
Marshall, Alice	£6-£8	Wiederseim, G.G.	£6-£8
Martin, L.B.	£5	Campbell's Soup advert	£35
Martineau, Alice	£5	Wilcock, A.M.	£3
Mauzan, A.	£3-£5	Williams, Madge	75p
Maybank, Thomas	£10-£15	Wuyts, A.	£3
Mercer, Joyce	£15-£20		
Miller, Hilda T., Liberty	£8		
other publishers	£5		
Nash, A.A.	£3		
Nixon, K.	£6		
Nystrom, Jenny	£4-£8		
O'Neill, Rose	£6+		
Outcault, R.F.	£2-£3		
Outhwaite, Ida Renthoul	£8-£10		
Overell, J.	£2		
Overnell	£2-£4		
Palmer, Phyllis M.	£3		
Parkinson, Ethel	£4-£8		
Paterson, Vera	£1.50		
Pearse, Susan B.	£4 -£8		
Piper, George	50p		
Plumstead, Joyce	£3-£5		
Poulbot, Francisque	£4		
Preston, Chloe	£5-£6		
Purser, Phyllis	£1.50-£2		
Rackham, Arthur	£20		
Richardson, Agnes	£3-£5		
Rose, Freda Mabel	75p		
Sandford, H. Dix	£4		
Smith, D. Carlton	£4		
Smith, Jessie Wilcox	£15		
Smith, May	£4-£5		
Sowerby, Millicent	£8		
chromo litho	£10		
Steele, L.	£2		
Sternberg, V.W. (VWS)	£2-£3		
Symonds, Constance	£5		
Tarrant, Margaret	£3-£6		
Taylor, A.	50p		
Tempest, Douglas	75p-£1.50		

Faulkner published Ethel Parkinson. £4

Different artists are now being collected. Some of the old favourites, such as Thackeray, McGill, and P.V. Bradshaw, and particularly 'Write-Aways' are coming back into popularity, but there is less interest in Bonzo, a state of affairs which is bound to be only temporary. Thematics such as cricket, football, corkscrews, dentistry and masonic, are going great guns.

THEMES

The more popular subjects which can be found on many different artists work. Account should be taken of the artist's value.

Angling	£2-£4
Aviation	£2.50-£4
Billiards/snooker	£5-£8
Cameras	£3-£6
Card games	£2-£4
Cats	£1.50-£4
Chess	£10-£20
Cigarette packets	£4-£6
'Coons'	£3-£6
Corkscrews	£6+
Cricket	£5-£10
Crossword puzzles	£4-£6
Cycling	£3-£5
Dentistry	£6-£8
Diabolo	£3-£6
Erotic	£1.50
Fleas	£1-£2
Football	£4-£6
Golf	£8-£15
Got any cigarette cards?	£12-£15
Gramophones	£3-£6
Hatpins	£1.50+
Hunting	£2-£4
Irish	50p-£1.50
Jewish	£6-£10
Lavatorial	75p-£1.50
Limericks	£3-£6
Maps	£2-£4
Masonic	£15
Match boxes	£3-£5
strikers	£8-£12
Military	£2-£4
Motoring	£2-£6
Motorcycling	£4-£6
Ping pong	£10-£25
Playing cards	£3-£6
Police	£2-£6
Postal	£2-£6
Postcards	£3-£6
Prehistoric	£3-£5
Pussyfoot	£2-£4
Railways	£2-£3
Rinking	£2-£6
Rugby	£4-£6
Scottish	50p-£1.50
Scouts	£5-£12
Smoking	£1.50-£3
Suffragettes	£8-£12
Telephones	£2-£4
Television	£1.50
Tennis	£2-£4
Trams	£1.50-£2.50
Welsh	50p-£1.50
Wireless	£3-£6

ARTISTS

A.E. (Archibald English)	£2
Adams, Will	£1.50
Anders, O.	£3-£5
Aris, Ernest	£4
Austerlitz, E.	£3
Bairnsfather, Bruce	£2.50-£6
Bamber, George A.	75p
Barnes, G.L.	£1
Bateman, H.M.	£3-£8
Becker, C.	50p
Bee	50p
Belcher, George	£3
Biggar, J.L.	£1-£1.50
Black, W. Milne (W.M.B.)	£3-£5
Bob	£1.50-£2.50
Boulanger, Maurice	£10-£15
Bradshaw, P.V. (P.V.B.)	£6
Broadrick, Jack	£1.50
Browne, Tom	£4+
Buchanan, Fred	£2-£3
Bull, Rene	£4
Buxton, Dudley	£2
Cameron, Archie	£1

COMIC

Carey, John	£1.50	Hebblethwaite, S.H.	£3-£5
Carnel, Albert	£3	Henry, Thomas	£3
Carter, Reg	£1.50-£3	Hilton, Alf	75p
Southwold Railway	£2-£4	Hughes, Lloyd	£1.50
Carter, Sydney	£1.50	Hurst, Hal	£3-£4
Cattley, P.R.	50p	Hyde, Graham	£4
Chalker	50p	Ibbetson, Ernest	£4-£8
Chandler, E.	£1	Karaktus	50p
Christie, G. Fyffe	£4-£6	Kennedy, A.E.	£3-£5
Cock, Stanley	£4	Kinsella, E.P.	£6-£15
Colbourne, Lawrence	£1.50	Kyd	£5-£8
Comicus	75p+	Leete, Alfred	£2-£4
Cook, C.K.	£4-£6	Lewin, F.G.	£4-£6
Cowham, Hilda	£3-£6	Ludgate	£2-£3
Crackerjack	£1.50-£2.50	Ludovici, A.	£3
Crombie, C.M.	£4-£8	Mac	£2
golf	£15	Mackain, F.	£1.50
Crow	£2-£4	Macleod, F.	75p
Cynicus		McGill, Donald	
court sized	£12	early, dated	£6
others	£2-£4	pre-1914	£4
Dauber	£2	later	£2-£3
Davey, George	£1.50-£2.50	'New'	50p
Dirks, Gus	£4-£6	Manavian, V.	£1
Duncan, Hamish	£2	Mason, Finch	£3
Dwiggins, C.V. (Dwig)	£5-£8	Mason, George W.	£4
Earnshaw, H.C.	£2-£3	Maurice, Reg	£1.50
Edwards, Lionel	£5	May, Phil	
Ellam (W.R.)	£3-£6	'Write-Away'	£6
Esmond, Germs series	£4	Oilette	£4
F.S.	£1-£1.50	Meredith, Jack	50p
F.W.	75p	Moreland, Arthur	£5
Fitzpatrick	50p+	Morgan, F.E.	£1.50-£2.50
Fleury, H.	£2.50-£4	Nap	£1.50-£3
Fuller, Edmund G.	£6	Noble, Ernest	£2-£4
Gill, Arthur	£3	Opper, F.	75p
Gilmour	75p	Outcault, R.F.	£2-£3
Gilson, T.	£2-£3	Owen, Will	£5
Gladwin, May	£2-£3	Parlett, Harry	75p+
Graeff	£2	Parlett, T.	50p
Grimes	£1	Payne, G.M.	£2-£4
Grin, C.V.	£1	Penny, Theo	75p
Guillaume, A.	£4-£10	Pirkis, coloured	£3
Halliday	£3	b&w	£2
Hardy, Dudley	£4	Pyp	£2
court size	£12	Quinton, Harry	75p
Hassall, John		Reynolds, Frank	£3
court size	£12	Right	75p-£1.50
others	£4	Roberts, Violet M.	£20

Robinson, W. Heath	£4-£6	White, Brian	£2
Rowland, Ralph	£1	Wilkins, Bob	£2.50
Rowntree, Harry	£8+	Wilkinson, Gilbert	£3
Sandford, H. Dix	£4	Wood, Lawson	£3-£4
Sarg, Tony	£3	Gran'pop	£3.50
Schonflug, Fritz	£3-£5	prehistoric	£4
Shaw, W. Stocker	£1.50-£2.50	Wood, Starr	£3
Shepheard, G.E.	£2-£4		
Smith, Syd	50p		
Spatz	£1		
Spurgin, Fred	£3		
Stoddart, R.W.	75p		
Studdy, G.E., 'Bonzo'	£4-£6		
others	£3-£5	E.J.H & Co., 'Ludgate' series	£2.50
Syd	75p	Good jokes from 'Punch'	£2.50-£3.50
Taylor A.	50p	T.B.M.	50p
Tempest, Douglas	75p-£1.50	Tuck Oilette, pickings from 'Puck'	£4
Thackeray, Lance, 'Write-Away'	£6	Wrench, good jokes from 'Punch'	£3
Oilette	£4	'Write-Away'	£2.50-£4
Thiele, A.	£15-£30	Other unlisted artists	30p+
Thomas, Bert	£1.50-£3	Unsigned	30p+
Ward, Dudley	£2-£3		

GENERAL

Non-artist signed cards and series, such as the 'Write-Away' types, (these have message to be completed by sender).

From an early Tuck Christmas set. Lance Thackeray is more collected now. £6

Barmen and not a pub in sight. £9

It's slightly damaged so this Kley is only £5

Paul Hey from 1900-01. £8

Picture Postcards were permitted as from 1st September 1894. Cards available before then were usually either postal stationery cards issued by the British Post Office, bearing a printed stamp (impression) or privately printed stationery postcards, sometimes with an illustration. There were also picture postcards, published mainly in Europe, which had either arrived by post or been brought back by travellers, thus stimulating the interest and demand for picture postcards in the U.K. It should be noted that many early postcard designs owe their origins to ephemera such as greetings cards, produced earlier.

The demand for these early cards is growing steadily, with Eastern European cards now selling along with the traditional Italian, French and Swiss. Early cards of the scarcer countries are eagerly sought

BRITISH CARDS

Court Sized (4.75"x 3.5")

Gruss Aus type, used	£15-£25
unused	£15
Other coloured types, used	£15-£25
unused	£15+
Other b&w types, used	£10-£15
unused	£8-£12

Expect to pay a premium for well collected towns. Cards used in 1894-5 are extremely rare and of considerable value.

Intermediate Sized

Vignette, coloured	£12-£15
b&w	£8-£12

Standard Sized (5.5"x 3.5")

Gruss Aus type	£15-£20
Vignette, coloured	£8-£12
b&w	£5-£8

The prices in this section refer to topographical types. For subject cards, see the appropriate sections.

EUROPEAN - GRUSS AUS

The prices below apply mainly to the German and Austrian Empires. See the Overseas Section for the more exotic countries.

Anniversaries	£20-£30
Exhibitions, coloured	£15-£30
b&w	£5-£15
Festivals	£15-£25
Parades	£12-£20
Royalty, commemorative	£12-£15
Souvenirs	£10-£15
Views, coloured	£5-£10
b&w	£4-£6

EUROPEAN - OTHER TYPES

Chromo-litho watercolour types

Swiss	£6-£12
French	£6-£10
Italian	£6-£8
Austrian/German	£4-£8

Artists

Cassiers, H.	£4+
Kley, Paul	£6
Loir, Luigi	£6
Wielandt, Manuel	£6

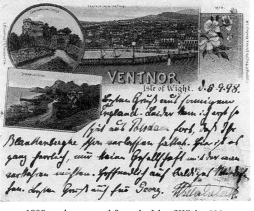

1898 used court card from the Isle of Wight. £20

137

JOSÉPHINE BAKER

£40 at least for Josephine Baker.

One of those themes which sells consistently well right across the board

ACTORS AND ACTRESSES

Baker, Josephine	£40
Bernhardt, Sarah	£8+
Coward, Noel	£3
Duncan, Isadora	£20
Hari, Mata	£20
Irving Henry, memorial card	£5
Langtry, Lily	£4
Embossed/applique	£2-£3
Play scenes	£1.50-£2.50
Portraits, misc	50p-£1

ADVERTISING

Posters, coloured	£8-£30
b/w	£4-£8
Playbill reproductions	£8-£15
Play scenes with advert	£2

ARTISTS

Bairnsfather, Bruce	£25-£35
Barribal, L.	£15-£25
Browne, Stewart	£8-£15
Browne, Tom	£10
Buchell, Charles	£10-£15
Hardy, Dudley	£8-£15
Hassall, John	£15-£25
Kennedy, A.E.	£8
Kinsella, E.P.	£12-£25
Morrow, Albert	£8-£10
Nerman	£20
Owen, Will	£8-£10
Pannett, R.	£10-£15
True, Will	£8-£10
Wood, Lawson	£10-£15

BALLET

Artistes

Genee, Dame Adelina	£8
Markova, Alicia	£6
Nijinsky	£50
Pavlova	£10
Companies/troupes	£4

Other artistes	£4-£8
Post war	£3-£5

CIRCUS

Animals, caged	£1.50+
Barnum and Bailey	
poster type	£25-£35
other	£15
Buffalo Bill's Wild West	
poster type	£15-£25
other	£10-£15
Clowns	
early	£8-£15
photographic performers	£8-£10
Freaks	
animal	£5-£15
human	£3-£8
giants	£3+
midgets/troupes	£3-£5
Miscellaneous advertising	
poster type	£15
Others	£6

FILM STARS

Prices quoted are for coloured cards except where noted.

Astaire, Fred	£4
Bogart, Humphrey	£6
Bergman, Ingrid	£3
Cagney, James	£5
Chaplin, Charlie, b&w	£5
red letter stills	£5
Crosby, Bing	£3
Davis, Bette	£3
Dean, James, b&w	£10
Dietrich, Marlene	£6
Flynn, Errol	£3
Gable, Clark	£2
Garbo, Greta	£8
Garland, Judy	£6
Harlow, Jean	£4
Keaton, Buster	£3
Laurel & Hardy	£15-£20
Lloyd, Harold	£3

ENTERTAINMENT

Lombard, Carole	£2
Marx Brothers	£8
Monroe, Marilyn	£10-£15
Temple, Shirley	£6
Valentino, Rudolph, b&w	£2-£4
Wayne, John	£6-£8
West, Mae	£5
Cowboy stars	£2-£4
Pre-1930 stars	£2-£3
Others, later	£2-£3
Film stills, b&w	£2-£4
Post-war 'pin-ups'	£1.50-£2.50

Concert parties, named troupes	£2-£4
Dancing, ballroom/stage etc.	£1
Escapologists/stuntmen	£10+
French showgirls	
A Travers Les Coulisses'	£6
Moulin Rouge, coloured	£6
portraits/miscellaneous	£2
Magicians/conjurors	£10-£20
Speciality acts	£3-£6
Ventriloquists	£10-£15

VARIETY ARTISTES

Bard, Wilkie	£3
Chevalier, Albert	£3
Chirgwin	£4
Elliott, G.H.	£4
King, Hetty	£5
Lauder, Harry	£3
comic	£2-£3
Leno, Dan	£3-£5
Lloyd, Marie	£5
Miller, Max	£5
Robey, George	£2
Stratton, Eugene	£4
Tate, Harry	£5
Tich, Little	£5

WIRELESS

Children's programmes	£2-£4
Radio celebrities	£2-£4
Studios	£2-£4
Wireless sets	£3-£6
QSL cards/radio amateurs	£1+
Comic sketches	£3-£6

MISCELLANEOUS

Acts/performers, professional	£2-£3
Amateur dramatics	25p+
Autographs, ink-signed,	
known stars	£2+
Bands	£4
Cabaret, French skeletons	£1-£2
other acts	£2-£4

SARAH BERNHARDT dans la Tosca.

Sarah Bernhardt always sells well. £8

Although there is a vast field here for collection and study, demand is mainly for Wembley. This section includes some outstanding designs, many of which are for overseas exhibitions. *See also silks.*

BRITISH

Festival of Britain, 1951
Signed watercolours	£6
Emmett, Roland	£4
Views	£2-£4

Wembley 1924/25
Views etc.	£1-£3
Overprinted cards	£10-£20
Product & company adverts	£10-£35
Queen's dolls house exhibition legend	£3

Other exhibitions, official cards
Before 1904	£2-£6
Later series	£1-£3
Advertising	£10-£25
Art types	£5-£20

Other exhibitions, unofficial cards
Photographs	£1-£3
Cards printed on stands	£4-£10
Franco-British (Mucha)	£100

FOREIGN

European
Before 1890	£25-£40
1890-1897	£15-£20
Paris 1900, chromo lithos	£10-£20
others	£2-£6
Later	£1-£8
Poster adverts	£15-£35

American
Columbian, 1893	£15
St Louis, 1904	£2-£6
Later, common cards	50p-£1
better cards	£2-£6

New Zealand 1906
Christchurch	£8-£12

Official postcard for the Fete des Vignerons Celebres in August, 1905

C.W.S. trade stand. £12

On board Shackleton's boat. £40

Some of Captain Buchanan's native helpers with some fine specimens in 1921. £5

EXPLORATION

There is an increased demand from existing collectors for used cards. Interesting and unusual material is being sought throughout the world and it is becoming difficult to obtain material for the advanced collector.

BELGIUM

1897 De Gerlache
Set/10, Nels, per card £50
Return of expedition, 1899 £40

FRANCE

1903 J B Charcot/'Francais'
Signed souvenir card
    of subscribers/Tuck £150
Launch of the 'Francais' 1903 £40
Set/20, per card £50
1903 on board the 'Francais' £40-£50

1908-1936 'Pourqoi-Pas' £35-£50
1934 Expedition, shipwreck 1936 £35
    funeral 1936 £60

Albert of Monaco/
    'Princess Alice' £25-£35

GERMANY

1901 On board the 'Gauss' £125

GREAT BRITAIN

1901-04 Scott/'Discovery'
On board the 'Discovery' £25
Links of Empire/Wrench, used
    from ports of call (set/ 4) £600
    unused £45
Canterbury Times views £40
'Terra Nova' (1910-1912) £15-£25
Memoriam card £20
Views of ships in British ports £25-£40
Ponting's official photos £10+

Bruce/'Scotia'
On board the 'Scotia' £40
Reliable Series set/12 £500

Shackleton
On board the 'Nimrod' 1908 £30
'Endurance' 1914-16 £15-£20
'Endurance' in ice £25+
Spratts Dog Food £20
Mrs Albert Broom photographs £15+
Exhibition £15

ITALY

1899 Abruzzi £35
On board the 'Stella Polare' £50
Rome conference 1901/
    subscription cards £40

1926 Nobile/Dirigible 'Italia' £45

NORWAY

1895 Nansen
On board the 'Fram' £40
Composite set 4 £400
Meissner & Buch (series 1016) £15-£20

1911 Amundsen/'Fram' £40

SWEDEN

1897 Andree/Hot Air Balloon to North Pole
Bergeret, Nancy (set/25) per card £60

1901-1903 Nordenskjold /
    'Antarctic' £50

U.S.A.

1903-1905 Ziegler/'America' £40

1908 Peary
S.S. 'Roosevelt/Peary portrait £8
Set/3, official, postally used
    12.9.09, per card £75
Peary & Cook/comic sketches £5-£10

EXPLORATION

1926 Byrd
Set/18, per card   £12

1934 Byrd   £8

EVEREST

1922 Expedition,
    group photograph,
    real photographic card   £8

1924 Expedition, per card   £8

SAHARA

1921 Capt. Angus Buchanan
Set/12, portraits & events
       per card   £5

Unusual 1922 Everest postcard. Published in France. £15

An 1898 winter in the Antarctic. £35

38

One of the leading themes. Includes the work of many artists as well as photographers, evidenced by the great numbers handed down to us. Glamour cards were collected mainly in France, or by our troops during the First World War.

BATHING

Early b&w	£1-£3
coloured	£4-£8
embossed	£6-£10
Glamour type	£1.50-£4
Photographic	£1-£3

PHOTOGRAPHIC

Bedroom and boudoir scenes	£4-£8
Nude studies, photographic	£8+
printed	£4-£6
Pornographic	£8+
Pretty girls	50p-£1

REPRODUCTIONS OF PAINTINGS

Reproductions, coloured	75p-£1.50
b&w	25p

ARTISTS

Abeille, Jack	£30-£35
Albertini	£4
Asti, Angelo	£6
Bailey, G.O.	£2
Balestrieri, L.	£5
Barber, C.W.	£3
Barribal, W.	£12-£15
Bianchi	£4
Boileau, Philip	£6
Bompard, S.	£5
Bottaro, E.	£5-£10
Bottomley, G.	£2-£3
Braun, W.	£5
Brown, Maynard	£2
Butcher, Arthur	£3
Carrere, F.O.	£6
Charlet, J.A.	£5
Cherubini, M.	£5
Christy, F. Earl	£4
Colombo, E.	£5-£6
Copping, Harold	£3

Corbella, T.	£5
Cremieux, Suzanne	£5
Crow	£2-£4
Diefenbach, K.W.	£5
Dufresne, Paul	£3
Fabiano, F.	£8-£10
Fidler, Alice Luella	£5
Fidler, Elsie Catherine	£4
Fisher, Harrison	£6
Fontan, Leo	£6-£8
Gayac	£15-£20
Gerbault, H.	£4
Gibson, Charles Dana	£3
Giglio	£3
Gilbert, Alan	£3
Greenbank, A.	£5
Guerzoni	£5-£8
Gunn, A.	£4
Hammick, J.W.	£2
Hardy, Dudley	£5+
Haviland, Frank	£5
Herouard	£12-£15
Horrell, Charles	£3
Horsfall, Mary	£3
Horwitz, Helena	£3
Icart, Louis	£15
Jafuri, R.	£4-£6
Jarach, A.	£6
Jay, Cecil	£5
Kaby	£4
Kaskeline, Fred	£4
Kimball, Alonzo	£2
Kirchner, Raphael	
middle period	£25-£35
later (Bruton Galleries)	£15-£30
Lasalle, Jean	£3
Le Munyon, Pearle Fidler	£5
Leonnec, G.	£10-£12
Lester, Ralph	£2
Lindsell, L.	£2
Lloyd, T. Ivester	£3
M.S.M.	£15-£20
Maillick, A.	£3
Marco, M.	£1.50

GLAMOUR

Marechaux, C.	£3-£5	Wennerberg, Brynoff	£10
Martineau, Alice	£6	Wichera, R.R.	£6-£10
Mauzan, A.	£5-£10	Wimbush, Winifred	£5
Mayer, Lou	£4-£6	Wuyts, A.	£4
Meunier, Suzanne	£15	Zandrino, Adelina	£5-£10
Milliere, Maurice	£10	Zirka, C.	£4
Monestier, C.	£3		
Monier, Maggy	£8		
Mostyn, Dorothy	£3		
Mostyn, Marjorie	£3		
Mouton, G.	£5-£8		
Naillod, C.S.	£4-£6		
Nam, Jacques	£6		
Nanni, G.	£5		
Ney	£8		
Nystrom, Henny	£6-£8		
Pannett, R.	£6		
Payne, G.M.	£3		
Peddie, Tom	£1.50-£2.50		
Pellegrini, E.	£12-£15		
Peltier, L.	£5		
Penot, A.	£10		
Pepin, Maurice	£8		
Peras	£5		
Person, Alice Fidler	£5		
Pillard	£5		
Quinnell, Cecil W.	£4		
Rappini	£4		
Rauh, Ludwig	£10		
Read, F.W.	£2		
Ribas	£6		
Robida, A.	£3		
Rodella, G.	£3		
Ryland, H.	£5-£8		
Sager, Xavier (Salt Lake)	£12		
Salmony, G.	£3		
Sand, Adina	£3		
Schubert, H.	£3-£5		
Scottie	£4		
Simonetti, A.M.	£3		
Solomko, Serge de	£8-£20		
Somerville, Howard	£3		
Spurgin, Fred	£3		
Stanlaw, S Penrhyn	£3		
Tam, Jean	£8-£10		
Terzi, A.	£5		
Underwood, Clarence	£5		
Usabal, Luis	£3-£6		
Vallet, L.	£5		

A rare Barribal with advertising for the
1912 Horse Show at Olympia. £25

These cards continue to sell steadily, which is not surprising considering the quality of most of them.

EMBOSSED

Chromo-litho	£5-£10
Other early types	£4-£6
Later types	£2-£4

FATHER CHRISTMAS

Early embossed	
red robes	£10-£12
other coloured robes	£12-£20
Hold to light	£50-£80
Non-embossed	£4-£10
Oilette	£8-£12
Photo type	£1-£2
Silks, First World War	£15

FLOWERS AND FRUIT

Coloured	75p-£2
Advertising	75p-£2.50

GREETINGS

Birthday	£2-£4
Christmas	£2-£5
Decoration Day	£5
Easter	£2-£6
bunnies	£3-£6
Faith, Hope & Charity, set/3	£5-£12
Frogs	£3-£10
Halloween	£4+
Independence Day	£4
Jewish New Year	£1-£4
New Year	£2-£4
Pigs	£4-£12
St. Patrick's Day	£3-£5
Thanksgiving	£4
Valentine's Day	£2-£6

LARGE LETTER/ALPHABET/DATES

Year dates, embossed type	£6-£10
hold to light	£15-£20
Calendar cards	£3-£6

Initials/alphabet/numbers	£2-£6
Initials, Tuck's 'Cherubs'	£6
Names of people	75p-£2
Names of places	£1.50+

LANGUAGE OF

Flowers, fruit, etc.	75p-£3
Stamps	£2-£3

ARTISTS

Barde	£1
Bayer, R.V.	£1.50
Billing, M.	£1
Boecker, A.G.	£1.50
Cane, Ella Du	75p
Craig, Janie	£3
Elliott, K.E.	75p
Foster, R.A.	75p
Golay, Mary	£2-£5
Guggenberger, T.	£10
Haller, A.	£1.50-£3
King, A. Price	75p
Klein, C., chromo-lithos	£3-£6
later issues	£2.50
Maguire, Bertha	75p
Mailick, A.	£3+
Millor	75p
Millot	75p
Muraton, E.	£1.50
Pressland, A.L.	£1.50
Renaud, M.	75p
Renault	75p
Short, E.A.	£1
Warrington, E.	50p

Although there is no sign of movement in literary cards, music continues to sell steadily with much interest in opera singers

LITERARY

Dickens
Characters	£2.50
Copping, H.	£4
'In Dickens Land'	
scenes	£2.50
views	£2
others	75p-£2.50
'Kyd'	£12
Tuck, early, numbered	£12

Shakespeare
Bates, M.	£4
C.W. Faulkner series	£5
Hildesheimer series	£1.50-£2.50
Nister, Ernest chromo-litho	£6
Oilette	£3
Tuck, early, numbered	£12

Miscellaneous
Alice in Wonderland	£4-£12
Bronte	50p+
Burns	50p+
Byron	£1+
Carlyle	50p+
Lorna Doone	£1-£2
Marie Corelli, set/6	£25
Poets/writers, early chromo-lithos	£6-£10
later portraits	£1-£2
Sherlock Holmes	£10-£15
Stevenson, R.L.	50p

Artists
Adams, Frank	£2.50
Bates, Marjorie C.	£4
Brundage, Frances	£3-£5
Copping, Harold	£4
Folkard, Charles	£8
Kyd	£12
Lovering	£1.50
Nixon, K.	£4
Quinnell, Cecil W.	£5
Richardson, R.W.E.	75p
Whitehead, Fred	£1

MUSICAL

Bands
Brass bands	£3
Champion bandsmen	£2
Composers, art	£3-£6
photographic	£2-£4
Dance, named	£5-£8
Gramophones	£3-£6
comic	£3-£6
Jazz, named and singers	£8+
Military bands	£6
Musical instruments	£1-£3
Orchestras, named	£2-£4
Organs	£2-£4

Opera
Adeline, Patti	£6
Sir Thomas Beecham Opera Co. (Rotary)	£3
Clara Butt	£3
Caruso	£10
Gigii	£4
Gilbert and Sullivan D'Oyly Carte Opera Co.	
Parkslee Pictures	£5
G.&.S photos	£3
Savoyard photos	£3
Melba	£6-£8
Tetrazzini	£6
Houses and concert halls	£2-£6

Song cards
Bamforths
set/3	£4
set/4	£6
odd cards	£1+
Feldman - per card	£2-£3
Tucks Illustrated Song Series	£2+
Others, per card	50p-£2

MILITARY

A tremendous lack of material makes it impossible to satisfy the demand for this subject, particularly for coloured regimental artist-drawn cards. Also a great demand for Russo-Japanese war cards caused by the blossoming of the Pacific rim market.

ABYSSINIAN WAR, 1939	£5-£10	Cartoons	£10-£25
		Hull trawler outrage	£3-£5
BOER WAR, 1899-1902		Photographs, etc.	£10+

SPANISH AMERICAN WAR, 1898

Cartoons
		£20-£30
coloured	£15-£25	
b&w	£12-£25	

Jamestown raid	£40	**SPANISH CIVIL WAR, 1935** £8-£15
St Helena, camps, etc.	£20+	
Tuck 'Empire'		**WORLD WAR I**
souvenir of 1900	£20	
peace card	£15	Aviation £2-£4
coloured	£15-£20	Belgian relief fund £1.50-£2.50
b&w	£12	refugees at named locations £10-£15
overprinted for victories	£15-£25	Campaign maps £2-£3
ships	£15+	Newspaper series showing events
Vignettes, coloured	£15-£25	e.g. Daily Mail £1-£2.50
b&w	£12-£20	Palestine £4-£15
War photographs	£8+	Personalities
		Lord Kitchener £2+
BOXER REBELLION, 1900		Kitchener, *In Memoriam* £3+
		Other war leaders
Cartoons, coloured	£25	British £2-£3
War photographs	£10+	others £1-£2
		Photographs of uniforms £2-£4
CHINESE CIVIL WAR, 1911-1917		POW's greetings, art £8-£12
		photographic £3-£4
Photographs, etc.	£10+	Regimental greetings cards £8-£12
		Tanks £2-£5
PATRIOTIC		Victory parades (London) 75p-£1.50
		War Bond campaign
Art type	£3-£6	Trafalgar Square £4-£6
Bulldogs	£3-£6	local visits £12-£20
Comics	£2-£4	Occupation of Germany £1-£3
Greetings and romantic	£1-£3	
Flags	£2-£4	**WORLD WAR II**
Royalty	£2-£3	
Anti British	£5-£10	Aviation £3-£6
Anti Kaiser	£3-£6	Germany, Nazi issues £8-£15
Czar of Russia	£8-£12	Great Britain
Russian revolution	£8-£15	comic £3-£6
		leaders £2-£4
RUSSO-JAPANESE WAR, 1905		Churchill £6-£20
		Netherlands

MILITARY

cartoons, anti-Nazi	£6-£8	history and traditions	£6
comics	£2.50	others	£6-£12
leaders (Allied)	£2-£3	Italian regimental cards, early	£4-£12
U.S.A., comic and patriotic	£2-£5	others	£2-£4
		Life in the army	£2-£4

ARTISTS

		Medals, Rees H.	
		present day war ribbons	£3
Bairnsfather, B.	£2.50-£6	daring deeds	£3
Baker, Granville H.	£4	V.C. winners	£6-£10
Bannister, A.F.D.	£4	Newspapers, reproductions	£2-£4
Becker, C.	£10	Recruiting posters	£15-£25
Beraud, N.	£3.50	Regimental badges (G&P)	£4-£8
Bourillon	£3	Royal Tournament, etc.	£1-£3
Chidley, Arthur	£10	Tuck Oilette	£3-£6
Copping, Harold	£3	Uniforms, scenes, etc., coloured	£3-£6
Cremieux, Suzanne		b&w and sepia	£1-£2.50
(Croix de Guerre des Allies)	£5	Vignettes, early	£8-£10
Dupuis, Emile	£5		
Gilson, T.	£2-£3		

Other

Henckle, Carl	£4	Army camps pre W.W.I, named	£3-£6
Holloway, Edgar A.	£6-£12	general barracks	£1.50-£2.50
Hudson, Gerald	£1.50	Red Cross	£3-£8
Ibbetson, Ernest	£6-£12	Regimental photographs	£2-£4

Leigh, Conrad	£1.50
Lloyd, T. Ivester	£3
Lumley, Savile	£3
McNeill, J.	£6-£10
Montague Love, H.	£6
O'Beirne, F.	£6-£12
Payne, Harry	
Tucks, early	£15-£35
Oilette	£5-£25
Badges and wearers	£8-£75
Stewart and Woolfe	£12
Gale and Polden	£12-£20
Pillard	£4
Rowlandson, G.D.	£3
Simkin, R.	£12
Stewart, J.A.	£4
Thiele, Arthur	£10-£15
Toussaint, M.	£6-£8
Ward, Herbert	£3
Woodville, R. Caton	£4

MISCELLANEOUS

Art types
Gale and Polden	
rates of pay cards	£15+

World War II comic. £2.50

Britain's answer to the Kaiser. £5.00

Banknotes	£4-£6
Cameras	£4-£8
advertising	£15-£30
comic	£3-£6
Caves	£1-£3
Chess	£15-£25
comic	£10-£20
Crossword puzzles	£4-£8
Diabolo	
comic	£3-£6
people playing	£1-£3
Esperanto	£5-£15
Executions	£8-£25
Friendly societies	£3-£12
Gambling and casinos	£2-£5
Gramophones, actual	£5-£8
comic	£3-£6
novelty records	£6-£8
Masonic	
comic	£15-£20
photographs	£3-£15
Newspaper facsimiles	
local	£6-£8
military	£4-£6
overseas	£5
Playing cards	£3-£15
Postcards	
advertising on reverse	£2-£6
comics	£2-£6
poster advertising	£15-£25
proofs and samples, etc.	£2-£6
travellers cards	£4-£8
Rinking	
comic	£2-£6
photographic	£2-£4
Round the world journeys	£8-£15
Smoking	
cigarette packets	£5+
comic	£1.50-£3
Got Any Cigarette Cards?	£12-£15
match boxes	£3-£5
match strikers	£8-£15
Telephones	£2-£4
comic	£2-£4
correspondence cards	£4-£8
Trees	£1-£3
Wireless	
comic	£3-£6
pictures of	£3-£6

At least this one didn't get Dutch elm disease. A bit better. £6

Sample from Blum & Degen. £2

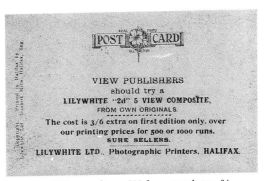

You could have as few as 500 from your photos. £4

1904 French used camera card. £4

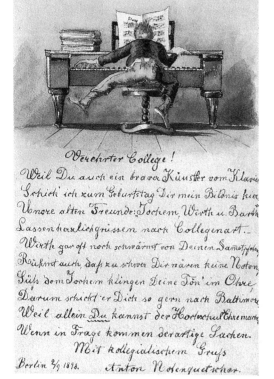

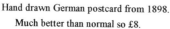

Hand drawn German postcard from 1898.
Much better than normal so £8.

Applique peacock. £8

German South West Africa is one of the better countries. £12

There is a steady demand for these interesting cards.

APPLIQUE

Feathers	£6-£10
Match strikers	£8-£15
Material	£2-£4
Metal models (cars, etc.)	£4
Real hair	£8
Stage stars	£2-£3
Stamp montage	£6-£12
Others	£1-£3

COIN & STAMP CARDS

Banknotes	£4-£6

Coins

National, embossed	£6-£8
printed	£6
Greetings	£3-£5

Stamps

Embossed (Zieher, O.)	£6-£8
other publishers	£4-£6
Printed (Zieher, O.)	£6+
other publishers	£4-£6
b&w printed	£2-£4

Certain countries, e.g. Canada realise a considerable premium.

COMPOSITE SETS

American sets	£20-£50
Early European sets, 3-5 cards (usually animals)	£30-£50
Large, 10-12 cards (Napoleon, Jean d'Arc, etc)	£50-£100
G P Govt Tea (Edward V11)	£120
Japanese	£20-£40

FANTASY

Enlarged objects (mainly North American)	£2-£4
Erotic	£5-£15
Faces in flowers	£3-£10
Faces in mountains, Killinger	£20-£25
later issues	£10-£15
Faces in smoke	£3-£5
Fantasy heads, coloured	£25-£35
b&w	£15-£30
Maps	£10-£15
Multi-babies	£3-£5
embossed	£6

HOLD-TO-LIGHT, (cut out type)

British views	£6+
Continental	£10-£15
Exhibitions	£12-£15
Flames	£15
Greetings, Father Christmas	£50-£80
cottages	£6
better designs	£15-£25

HOLD-TO-LIGHT, (mechanical)

Blow out type	£10
Kaleidoscopes	£25-£35
Lever change	£3-£6
Paper decorations	£10-£20
Roller blinds (early German)	£30
Rotating/calendar	£6-£15
Venetian blinds	£3+

PULL OUTS

Animals	£2.50
Beer bottles	£3
Buses	£4
Cats and dogs	£2.50+
Comic	£2.50-£3.50
Father Christmas	£6+
Fortune telling	£5
Hop-picking	£4-£6
Irish shamrocks, etc.	£2.50
Military, camps	£3-£4
soldiers	£3
Motor cars	£3.50
Postmen, mail vans, etc.	£4-£6
Railway tickets, named	£2.50
Teddy bears	£6-£8
Town views, multi-view fronts	£2-£3.50
Trams	£4
Welsh ladies	£2-£3.50

NOVELTY

TRANSPARENCIES

British views (colour change)	£4
British views, meteor, published by	
Hartmann	£8
greetings (Father Xmas)	£12-£15
others	£6-£12
Continental	£10-£15
Exhibitions	£12-£15
Meteors	£10-£15
Puzzles	£4+

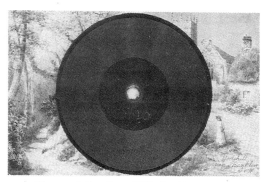

The record plays 'Poor Old Joe' and is worth £6.

MISCELLANEOUS

Aluminium	£4
Bas relief	£2
Bookmark and midgets	£3
Celluloid	£5
embossed	£8
Cut out models	
Tuck, W.E. Mack,	
Jas Henderson, etc.	£30-£75
Star series, animals	£10
later issues, Salmon	£4-£6
Glass eyes	£4-£6
Gramophone records	£6-£8
Hand painted	£4-£6
Invisible picture (coin rub)	£4-£6
Japanese laquered	£4+
Jigsaw puzzles (Tuck)	£10-£15
others	£8+
Leather	£4+
Mirrors	£1
Peat (Irish)	£3
Perfumed	£2-£4
Pop-ups	£5-£10
Puzzles	£2-£4
Rice paper -Oolong Tea	£8-£15
Shapes	£4-£10
Stereo views	£3-£6
Squeakers	£3+
3D types, complete with eyepiece	£6-£8
Wagging tails, spring	£3
Wood	£4

Aitutaki became part of the Cook Islands in the 1930s. £25

Angolan cyclists. Very scarce. £10

Used prices refer to cards used in *country of origin* and with the stamp attached (and intact), if one was originally on the card. It is also worth noting that the prices given in this section reflect the market in Britain. Cards sometimes fetch more in Britain than in their country of origin and vice versa. Because of the international nature of the trade in overseas cards, currency fluctuations can also affect prices dramatically.

	UNUSED	USED		UNUSED	USED
			street scenes	£2+	
Aden	**75p**	**£1.50**	**Austria**	**35p**	**35p**
early	£4		ethnic	£2	
events	£3		folklore	£2	
Abyssinia *see under Ethiopia*			Gruss Aus	£4+	
Afghanistan	**£2**	**£6**	industrial	£2+	
Afghan war	£3.50		railway	£2.50+	
ethnic	£2.50		street scenes	£1+	
Albania	**£2**	**£3**	**Austrian Levant**	**£1.50**	**£3.50**
ethnic	£2.50		**Azores**	**£1**	**£1.50**
street scenes	£3		**Bahamas**	**£2.50**	**£3.50**
Aldabra Islands	**£10**	**£20**	1933 hurricane	£8	
Algeria	**25p**	**35p**	American coloured types	£3	
Andaman Islands	**£5**	**£15**	ethnic	£4+	
Andorra			military	£8	
French	£2.50	£3	street scenes	£4	
Spanish	£2.50	£3	**Bahrain**	**£8**	**£25**
street scenes	£3		**Barbados**	**£1**	**£2.50**
Angola	**£1.50**	**£3**	early	£20	
Portuguese Congo	£2	£5	ethnic	£3	
Angra	**£3**	**£5**	railway	£8+	
Anguilla	**£8**	**£25**	street scenes	£3	
early	£10		**Barbuda**	**£10**	**£30**
Antigua	**£3**	**£6**	**Basutoland**	**£2**	**£20**
early	£5		ethnic	£3	
street scenes	£4		named places	£3.50	
Argentine	**50p**	**50p**	**Batavia** *see Netherlands Indies*		
ethnic	£2		**Bechuanaland**	**£3**	**£25**
Gruss Aus	£8		ethnic	£2.50	
railway	£3.50		named places	£6	
street scenes	£1+		**Belgium**	**35p**	**35p**
Ascension	**£8**	**£30**	canals	£1.50+	
royal visit	£30	£175	costumes	£1+	
Australia	**50p**	**50p**	dog carts	£3+	
Aborigines	£4		explosions	£3+	
animal teams	£3.50		farming/industry	£2+	
bush life	£3		occupations	£2+	
early	£8+		railway engines	£2.50+	
Fullwood, A.H.	£6-£15		street fairs/markets	£3+	
mining	£4+		street scenes (cities)	50p+	
postal stationery	£15+		street scenes (towns/villages)	£1.50+	
railway officials	£6+				
railway stations	£6				

An itinerant French musician. £3.50

Rough justice in Persia. £10

Whaling always sells. £30

	UNUSED	USED
Benin *see Dahomey*		
Bermuda	£1	£1.50
Boer War	£20	
early USA types	£7+	
ethnic	£4+	
street scenes	£4+	
Bhutan	£3	£25
ethnic	£3.50	
Bolivia	£2	£3.50
early	£4	
ethnic	£2.50	
railway	£5	
street scenes	£3.50	
Bosnia and Herzegovina	£2	£3
Brazil	75p	£1
early	£8	
ethnic	£2+	
railway	£3.50	
street scenes	£2	
British Guiana	£2	£4
early	£8	
ethnic	£3	
industrial	£5	
penal settlements	£5	
railway	£6	
river steamers	£5	
street scenes	£3.50	
British Honduras	£8	£15
early	£12	
ethnic	£8	
gold mining	£10	
railway	£10	
street scenes	£9	
British Levant	£1.50	£2
British Somaliland	£10	£30
Brunei	£9	£30
Bulgaria	£1	£1
early	£3	
ethnic	£1.50	
street scenes	£1.50	
Burma	75p	£1
early	£2.50	
ethnic	£1.50	
street scenes	£1	
Cambodia	75p	£2
Cameroons (French)	£1.50	£2.50
Cameroons (German)	£4	£8
Canada	35p	35p

	UNUSED	USED
disasters	£4	
Indians	£2+	
lake steamers	£2+	
mining	£2+	
occupations	£2+	
patriotic	£5+	
railway engines	£2+	
railway stations	£3+	
street scenes	£2	
Canal Zone	£1	£1.50
ethnic	£2	
Canary Islands	£1	£1
ethnic	£2	
Gruss Aus	£5	
street scenes	£2	
Cape Verde Islands	£1	£2
Caroline Islands	£8	£25
Cayman Islands	£10	£20
1940 photo types	£8	
Ceylon	35p	50p
Boer war	£10	
early	£2	
Chad	75p	£1
Chile	75p	£1.50
early	£8	
earthquakes	£3.50	
ethnic	£2	
railway	£3+	
street scenes	£2	
China	£1.50	£2
ethnic	£2	
street scenes	£2	
used at **French P.O.**		£6
used at **German P.O.**		£7
used at **Italian P.O.**		£7
used at **Japanese P.O.**		£15
used at **Russian P.O.**		£15
used at **American P.O.**		£15
Christmas Island	£20	£30
1950's Atom bomb test	£6	
Cocos Keeling Islands	£20	£40
Colombia	£2	£3.50
ethnic	£3	
railway	£3	
street scenes	£3	
Comoro Islands	£2.50	£6
Congo, French & Belgian	75p	£1.50
postal stationery	£1.50	£2

Maltese Gruss Aus. Always well collected. £30

Postally used from New Caledonia. £8

A young Rhodesian lady. £6

Black humour. £10

Art Deco artist Mela Koehler. £65

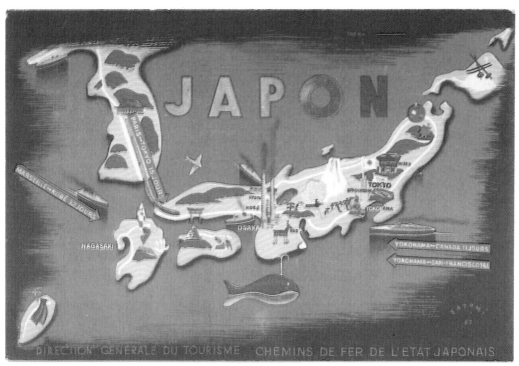

The Olympics that never happened. Japan 1940. £30

Composite set. £50

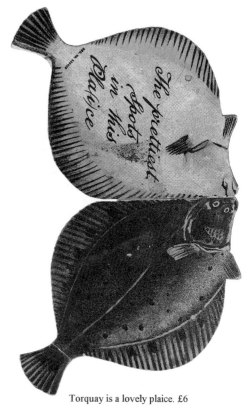

Torquay is a lovely plaice. £6

A typical Christmas Hold to Light. Still cheap at £5

54

Cats at their best. £10

Winter sport? £18

From Tuck set 8727 ' The iron walls of England'. £6

A Lance Thackeray 'write-away' table tennis comic. Very rare. £25

Hartmann published Orang Utang. £5

A better greetings card from about 1907. £6

Answer. Go to postcard fairs. Chloe Preston from 1925. £5

One of the Tuck Aesop's Fables series by Sancha. £10

The Colours.

From Tuck set 9885. £8

Surrey Lanes sell for £6-£8

Seaforth Highlanders. £8

Mabel Lucie Attwell and golf are both good sellers. £8

German military. £8

A better 'in flames' silk. £50

Father Christmas. Always popular. £4

A Merry Christmas. to you.

And you thought New Year was a good holiday in Scotland! £8

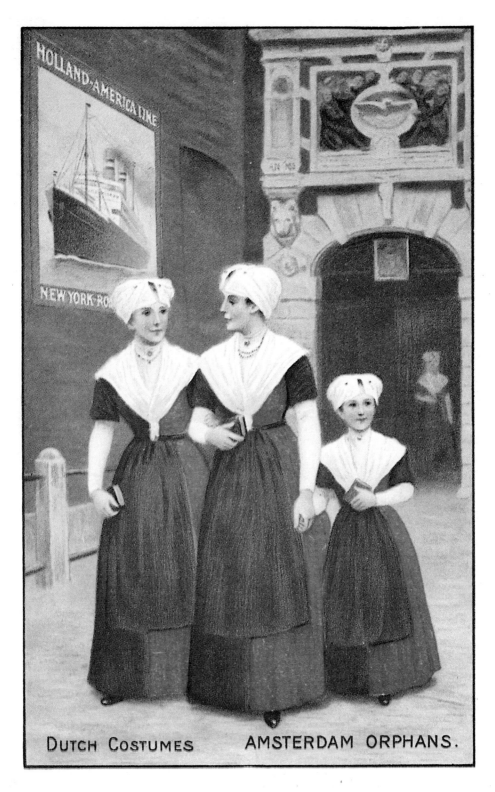

A very subtle Dutch shipping advert. £30

MR. GOBBLE-GOBBLE TURKEY, THOUGH YOU'RE VERY PROUD AND FINE,
WONT YOU TAKE THIS LUMP OF SUGAR? WILL YOU BE A FRIEND OF MINE?

A rare Millicent Sowerby from the Farmyard Animals set. £8

Theatre poster from Tuck Celebrated Poster set 1501. £45

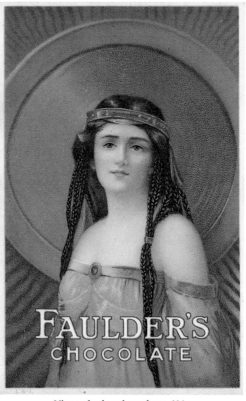

Nice early chocolate advert. £30

Made in France about 1916. Rare regimental silk. £45   Almost every home had one. Singer ad is £25.

On the flat from series 901/d. £4

One of Donald McGill's many World War One comic cards for Inter Art. £4

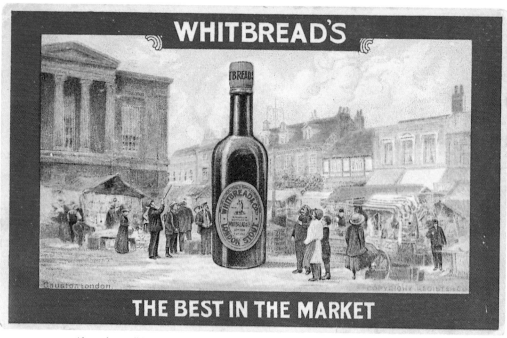

Almost impossible to find in good condition. They weren't made of very stout card. £25

French produced Nini Hager art nouveau. £50

NO T'ANKS.

1917 comic tank. £4

L.A. Govey comic with postal and military interest. £5

THE NORTH BRITISH RAILWAY.
LOTHIAN COAST EXPRESS.

A big change from the electric train that runs on the Edinburgh coast line today. £3.50

SILVIA

E. Lancombe glamour published by Savory of Bristol. £20

Offensive Générale   General offensive

WW1 Xavier Sager. £10

One of the Misch & Stock 'Addled Ads'. £4

Rumanian Gruss Aus. £12

1908 Franco British Exhibition Entente Cordiale. £12

Chamberlain and his Trade Tarrif Act by Dudley Ward. £6

Faulkner published anonymous glamour. £10

Circa 1905 greetings. Printed in Berlin. £1.50

Emigrate to Canada by Cunard. £28

A real Heath Robinson postcard. £5

Postally used Madagascar. The picture side is a bit better so £4

Nice railway cards always sell as does Greece. £20

	UNUSED	USED
Cook Islands	£8	£15
Corfu	75p	£1
street scenes	£2	
Costa Rica	£1.50	£3
early	£6	
earthquake	£4	
ethnic	£2.50	
street scenes	£3	
Crete	£3.50	£4
ethnic	£4	
military	£4	
street scenes	£4	
used at **Austrian P.O.**		£18
used at **French P.O.**		£12
used at **Italian P.O.**		£12
Cuba	£1	£1
early	£3+	
street scenes	£2	
Curacao *see Netherlands Indies*		
Cyprus	£4	£6
ethnic	£6	
railway	£18	
street scenes	£6	
Czechoslovakia	50p	75p
street scenes	£1	
Dahomey Benin	£3	£4
street scenes	£4	
Danish West Indies	£4	£12
street scenes	£5	
Danzig	£1.50	£3
Denmark	75p	75p
street scenes	£1.50	
Dar-es-Salaam *see German East Africa*		
Djibouti	75p	£1
Dominica	£2.50	£4
Dominican Republic	£2	£4
Easter Island	£8	£20
Ecuador	£1.50	£3.50
early	£3	
ethnic	£3	
railway	£5	
street scenes	£3	
Egypt	30p	30p
canal	50p	
early, coloured	£2.50+	
ethnic	75p	
street scenes	75p	
used at **Turkish P.O.**		£15

	UNUSED	USED
El Salvador	£1.50	£3
early	£3.50	
ethnic	£2	
railway	£4	
street scenes	£3.50	
Equatorial Guinea	75p	£1.50
Eritrea	£1.50	£4
Estonia	£1.50	£1.50
street scenes	£2	
used with **Russian** *stamps*		£3.50
Ethiopia	£2.50	£10
Falkland Islands	£10	£30
Antarctic expeditions	£25+	
early vignettes	£15	
events	£20+	
panorama cards	£35+	
penguins/birds	£6	
sheep industry	£10	
ships	£12+	
whaling	£15+	
Fanning Island	£10	£25
Faroe Islands	£10	£25
Fernando Poo	£2.50	£4
Fez *see Morocco*		
Fiji	£2	£3
ethnic	£3	
named villages	£4	
visit of Australian Fleet	£10	
Finland	£1.50	£2
costumes	£1.50	
Gruss Aus	£8	
street scenes	£3	
Fiume	£2	£3
Formosa	£4	£15
France	25p	25p
buses	£4+	
canals	£2+	
industrial	£2+	
railway	£2+	
social history	£2+	
street scenes, cities	25p-£1.50	
street scenes, towns	50p-£3	
Street scenes, villages	£2+	
trams	£2+	
French Guiana	£1.50	£2.50
French Guinea	75p	£1.50
French Indian Settlements	£1	£2.50
French Oceanic Settlements	£5	£6

	UNUSED	USED		UNUSED	USED
French Somali Coast	£1	£1.50	ethnic	£3	
French Sudan	£1	£1.50	railway	£5	
Funchal	£2	£4	street scenes	£3	
Gambia	£6	£12	**Hainan Island**	£6	£20
German East Africa	£3	£10	**Haiti**	£3	£3.50
early	£8		**Hawaii**	£2	£2.50
military	£4		ethnic	£2.50	
German New Guinea	£7	£25	street scenes	£3.50	
early	£10		**Hedjaz** *see Saudi Arabia*		
ethnic	£7		**Heligoland**	£2	£2.50
villages	£8		**Honduras**	£1.50	£2.50
German South West Africa	£3.50	£10	early	£3.50	
military	£5		ethnic	£2	
street scenes	£5		railway	£5	
Germany	25p	25p	street scenes	£2.50	
costumes	£1.50		**Hong Kong**	£3	£3.50
disasters	£2.50		early	£8+	
Gruss Aus	£4+		ethnic	£3	
industrial	£2.50+		railway	£5	
occupations	£2.50+		street scenes	£5	
street scenes	75p+		**Horta**	£3	£5
Gibraltar	50p	50p	**Hungary**	75p	75p
events	£2.50		early	£3+	
silks	£18		ethnic	£1.50	
street scenes	£1		street scenes	£1.50	
Gilbert & Ellice Islands	£8	£30	**Iceland**	£2.50	£8
Goa *see Portuguese India*			ethnic	£3.50	
Gold Coast	£3	£3.50	railway	£15	
early	£10		street scenes	£5	
ethnic	£3		**India**	30p	30p
events	£6		early	£2	
military	£4		ethnic	30p	
railway	£6		street scenes	50p	
street scenes	£4		**Indo-China** *see Cambodia, Laos, and Vietnam*		
Greece	£1	£1	**Indonesia** *see Netherlands Indies*		
embossed Postal Stationery	£8	£8	**Iran** *see Persia*		
ethnic	£2		**Iraq**	£1	£1.50
Salonika campaign	£1		British occupation	£1.50	
street scenes	£3.50		dvents	£3.50	
Greenland	£5	£25+	street scenes	£2	
ethnic	£6		**Italy**	25p	25p
Grenada	£3	£6	costumes	75p	
early	£5		disasters	£2+	
street scenes	£4		early	£2+	
Guadeloupe	£1	£1.50	social history/industrial	£3+	
Guam	£6	£20	street scenes	50p-£2.50	
Guatemala	£2	£3.50	**Ivory Coast**	£1	£1.50
early	£4		**Jamaica**	75p	£1.50

A Belgian dog cart. Some of these are very common. £6

Souvenir of the first flight to New Caledonia from Paris. £25

Dominican Gruss Aus type. Early, so £4.

Muscat is rare. £8

Boat building in Greece. £8

Postally used real photo of Salisbury, Rhodesia.
A bit better. £4

The Icelandic parliament in 1918. £10

A Nyasaland railway station. £15

	UNUSED	USED		UNUSED	USED
early	£5		rubber collecting	£2	
earthquakes	£3		street scenes	£3.50	
street scenes	£3	**Maldive Islands**	£10	£25
Japan	50p	75p	**Malta**	50p	50p
ethnic	75p		early (vignettes on postal		
street scenes	75p		stationery)	£40	
Java	£1	£1.50	early (vignettes)	£25	
Johore *see Malaya*			later coloured cards	50p	
Jordan	£1.50	£2	military (photographic)	£4	
Kedah *see Malaya*			panorama cards	£15	
Kelantan *see Malaya*			shipping (including naval)	£4	
Kenya	£1	£2	street scenes (photographic)	£5	
ethnic	£2		**Manchuria** *see China*		
military	£4		**Marshall Islands**	£8	£25
street scenes	£3		**Martinique**	75p	£1.50
Korea	£3	£15	street scenes	£2	
ethnic	£4		**Mashonaland** *see Rhodesia*		
street scenes	£4		**Matabeleland** *see Rhodesia*		
Used at **Japanese P.O.**		£20+	**Mauritania**	£1	£1.50
Kuwait	£8	£30	**Mauritius**	£3	£3.50
Labuan	£15	£30	early	£6	
Laccadives Islands	£6	£15	events	£7	
Laos	£2	£2.50	railway	£8	
Latvia	£1.50	£2	street scenes	£4	
street scenes	£3		**Memel**	£2	£4
used with **Russian** *stamps*		£3.50	**Mexico**	50p	75p
Lebanon	£1	£2.50	ethnic	£1.50	
ethnic	£2		military	£4	
street scenes	£2		railway	£4	
Liberia	£5	£10	street scenes	£2	
early	£12		**Monaco**	50p	50p
Libya	75p	75p	street scenes	60p	
Liechtenstein	£2	£2.50	**Montenegro**	£1.50	£2.50
Lithuania	£2	£3.50	**Montserrat**	£6	£15
street scenes	£3		riot	£10	
used with **Russian** *stamps*		£4	**Morocco**	35p	35p
Lord Howe Island	£6	£20	*used at* **British P.O.**		£3
Lourenco Marques	£2	£4	*used at* **German P.O.**		£4
Loyalty Islands	£4	£15	*used at* **Spanish P.O.**		£3
Luxembourg	£1	£1	**Mozambique**	£2	£3
Macao	£6	£18	**Muscat**	£8	£60
street scenes	£10+		**Nauru**	£10	£50
Madagascar	75p	£1.50	postal stationery	£30	
Madeira	£1	£2	**Nepal**	£3	£8
Malaya (including States)	£2	£3+	**Netherlands**	25p	25p
early	£8		canals	£2.50+	
ethnic	£3		ethnic	£2.50+	
railway	£8				

OVERSEAS

A Russian market trader from 1905. £4

It's probably a British built locomotive. In the Sudan, £6

At the regatta at Macassar. £4

Glencoe, Illinois circa 1928. £3

Talbot House in Sliema, Malta. £3

Ivory trade in the Belgian Congo. £2.50

	UNUSED	USED		UNUSED	USED
industrial	£1.50+		Halleys Comet	£16	
railway stations	£1.50+		**Pahang** see *Malaya*		
street scenes	50p+		**Palestine**	50p	50p
windmills	50p		Gruss Aus	£8+	
Netherlands Indies	£1	£2	military	£4+	
Nevis	£5	£25	street scenes	£4+	
New Britain see *New Guinea*			**Panama**	£1	£2
New Caledonia	£2.50	£8	ethnic	£2.50	
street scenes	£4		railway	£3	
Newfoundland	£3	£3.50	street scenes	£3	
New Guinea	£6	£25	**Papua**	£5	£25
ethnic	£6		ethnic	£6	
named villages	£8		**Paraguay**	£2	£3
New Hebrides	£6	£15	early	£4	
New Zealand	35p	50p	ethnic	£3	
disasters	£3+		railway	£5	
Fullwood, A.H.	£6		street scenes	£3.50	
industrial	£3+		**Pemba Island**	£10	£25
Maori	£2		ethnic	£12	
occupations	£3+		**Perim Island**	£6	£25
railway stations	£6+		early	£12	
street scenes	75p+		**Persia**	£3.50	£6
Nicaragua	£3	£6	*postal stationery*	£20	£20
early	£8		**Peru**	£1	£2.50
ethnic	£4		early	£6	
street scenes	£4		ethnic	£3.50	
Nicobar Islands	£10	£15	railway	£5	
Niger	75p	£1.50	street scenes	£3.50	
Nigeria	£1	£1.50	**Phillipines**	£1.50	£2
early	£5		**Pitcairn Islands**	£8	£40+
ethnic	£3		earlier cards	£15	
events	£4		ethnic	£20	
military	£4		**Poland**	50p	50p
railway	£5		early	£3.50	
street scenes	£3.50		ethnic	£2	
Niue	£10	£25	street scenes	£2.50	
Norfolk Island	£20	£35	*used with* **Russian** *stamps*		£2
Kingsford Smith flight	£50		**Ponta Delgada**	£3	£5
whaling	£35		**Portugal**	50p	50p
North Borneo	£6	£15	ethnic/industrial	£3.50	
ethnic	£8		Gruss Aus	£4	
street scenes	£8		railway stations	£4	
Norway	35p	35p	street scenes	£2	
early (Hilsen Fra)	£8+		**Portuguese India**	£1	£2.50
street scenes (cities)	£2		**Puerto Rico**	£3	£4
Nyasaland	£3	£15	street scenes	£4	
Nyassa Company	£5	£8	**Punta Arenas** see *Chile*		
Ocean Island	£8	£30	**Quelimane**	£5	£15

OVERSEAS

	UNUSED	USED		UNUSED	USED
Raratonga see Cook Islands			street scenes	£6	
Reunion	£2.50	£4	**Selangor** see Malaya		
Rhodesia	£1	£1.50	**Senegal**	75p	£1
ethnic	£2		**Serbia**	£2	£3
street scenes	£5+		ethnic	£3	
Rumania	75p	£1	street scenes	£3	
early	£3.50		**Seychelles**	£4	£15
ethnic	£3		political prisoners	£15	
street scenes	£2		street scenes	£8	
Russia	£1	£1.50	undivided backs	£10	
civil War	£10		**Siam** see Thailand		
expeditionary forces	£8		**Sierra Leone**	75p	£1.50
Gruss Aus	£8		ethnic	£2	
industrial/ethnic	£3.50		military	£4	
occupations	£4		railway	£4	
railway stations	£5		street scenes	£3	
street scenes	£4		**Sikkim**	£4	£30
St.Christopher see St.Kitts			**Singapore**	£2	£3
St.Croix see Danish West Indies			artist drawn	£8	
St.Helena	£2.50	£10	early	£15	
Boer war	£15		ethnic	£4	
street scenes	£4		Raffles Hotel	£6	
St.Kitts	£4	£10	railway stations	£18	
early	£8		street scenes	£7	
street scenes	£5		**Solomon Islands**	£10	£30
St.Lucia	£3	£3.50	**Somalia**	75p	£1.50
Boer War	£20		**South Africa**	50p	50p
coaling/shipping	£4		ethnic	75p	
early	£8		mining	£2	
events	£6		railway	£4	
St.Martin see Danish West Indies			street scenes	£2	
St.Pierre et Miquelon	£5	£10	**South Georgia** see Falkland Islands		
St.Thomas & Prince Island	£4	£6	**South West Africa** see German South West		
St.Vincent	£4	£10	Africa		
early	£10		**Spain**	25p	25p
eruption	£6		costumes	£1+	
street scenes	£5		Gruss Aus	£3+	
St.Vincent CV see Cape Verde Is.			railway stations	£4+	
Salvador see El Salvador			Spanish civil war	£8+	
Samoa	£6	£15	street scenes	£1+	
early	£10		**Spanish Guinea (Rio Muni)**	£2.50	£4
ethnic	£6		**Straits Settlements** see Malaya		
street scenes	£6		**Sudan**	£1.50	£2
Samos	£5	£18	ethnic	£2	
San Marino	£2	£3	military	£4	
Sarawak	£6	£20	river steamers	£4	
street scenes	£8		**Sumatra**	£2	£3
Saudi Arabia	£3	£25	**Surinam**	£1	£1.50

	UNUSED	USED
Swaziland	£5	£20
ethnic	£6	
named villages	£6	
Sweden	30p	30p
costumes	75p+	
Hilsen Fra	£10	
street scenes	£1+	
Switzerland	35p	40p
costumes	£1+	
Gruss Aus	£5+	
industrial/ethnic	£3+	
lake steamers	£1.50+	
railways	£2+	
street scenes	£2+	
Syria	£1	£2
Tahiti	£5	£6
Tanganyika	£1	£2
ethnic	£2	
street scenes	£3	
Tangier *see Morocco*		
Tasmania *see Australia*		
Tete	£5	£15
Thailand	£6	£8
street scenes	£7	
Thursday Island	£10	£20
Tibet	£3	£30
ethnic	£3.50	
towns	£6	
Tierra del Fuego *see Argentina/Chile*		
Timor	£4	£15
Tobago	£4	£6
Togo (British/German)	£4	£12
Togo (French)	£2.50	£3.50
Tonga	£7	£20
postal stationery	£20	
Trengganu *see Malaya*		
Trinidad	75p	£1
1933 hurricane	£5	
early	£10	
ethnic	£2	
oil fields	£2	
street scenes	£2	
Tristan da Cunha (pre 1928)	£100	
Tunisia	25p	25p
Turks and Caicos Islands	£15	£25
Turkey	35p	50p
ethnic	£1+	
street scenes	£1+	

	UNUSED	USED
used at **Austrian P.O.**		£4
used at **British P.O.**		£2
used at **French P.O.**		£2
used at **German P.O.**		£3
used at **Italian P.O.**		£3
used at **Polish P.O.**		£50
used at **Rumanian P.O.**		£25
used at **Russian P.O.**		£8
Uganda	£2	£2.50
ethnic	£3	
street scenes	£3	
U.S.A.	35p	35p
disasters	£1+	
Innes, John	£3-£5	
railway stations (cities)	50p	
railway stations (towns)	£2+	
steamboats	£2+	
street scenes (photographic)	£3+	
Upper Volta	£1	£4
Uruguay	75p	75p
ethnic	£1	
railway	£4	
street scenes	£3+	
Vietnam	£1.50	£2
Virgin Islands (British)	£10	£25
Virgin Islands (American)	£2	£5
Yemen	£3	£10
Yugoslavia	50p	75p
ethnic	75p	
street scenes	£1.50	
Zambezi	£5	£15
Zanzibar	£1.50	£2
early	£3.50	
railway	£6	
street scenes	£3	
used at **French P.O.**		£6
Zululand	£5	£25

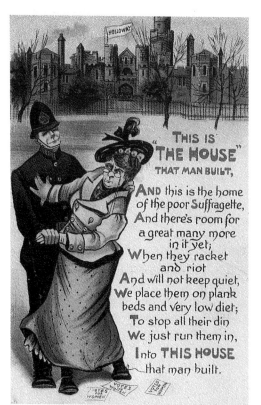

THIS IS "THE HOUSE" THAT MAN BUILT,

AND this is the home of the poor Suffragette, And there's room for a great many more in it yet; When they racket and riot And will not keep quiet, We place them on plank beds and very low diet; To stop all their din We just run them in, Into THIS HOUSE that man built.

THIS IS "THE HOUSE" THAT MAN BUILT

THE HOUSE that our Statesmen for years have controlled Ruling the world with mind fearless and bold; Can Woman expect To rule such a HOUSE, She that's afraid of a poor little mouse: No! No!! Suffragette your place is not yet, Inside THE HOUSE that man built.

This is "THE HOUSE" that man built, And these are the Suffragettes of note Determined to fight for their right to vote; For they mean to be, each one an M.P. And they'll keep their vow some fine day you'll see, For the Suffragette is determined to get Into "THE HOUSE" that man built.

This is "THE HOUSE" that man built, And this is the Flag of the Woman's Franchise, Which is making our Ministers open their eyes: Fighting with grit, to the front bit by bit, Determined in Parliament one day to sit, The bold Suffragette who is sure to get yet Into "THE HOUSE" that man built.

There are twelve in this set of Suffragette comics. In good condition they sell for £15 each

Apart from a resurgence in the interest in suffrage where so much material went into collections some years ago, particularly in America, very little in this category is being sought. The demand for Churchill has ceased.

Acts of Parliament

Free trade	£3-£8
National Insurance acts	£4-£6
Shops Act	£4
Workers compensation	£3-£4
Others	£3+

Alsace Lorraine 1903 £4-£8
    Hansi £12-£15

Bulgaria 1903 £8

Dreyfus 1899 £10-£15
    cartoons £15-£25

Events

Canvassing/candidates	£8+
Declarations	£10-£15
Evictions	£25-£50
Strikes and marches	£10-£40
Liverpool	£25-£50
coal picking	£35-£60
Sydney Street Siege, 1912	£4-£8
Treaties	£3-£5

Irish Home Rule

Cartoons	£10-£20
Easter Rising ,1916	£4-£6
Leaders	£10-£15
Mourning cards	£15+
Gun running	£10-£15
Ulster campaign	£10-£15

National Socialist Party

British, Mosley	£10-£15
German, Nazi Party	£8-£20
Italian, Mussolini	£4-£6

Suffragette Campaigns

Action	£20-£30
Cartoons	£15-£20
Comic	£8-£12
Leaders	£15-£25
Publicity cards	£15-£25

World War I

Edith Cavell	
Corbella set	£40
grave	£3
mourning cards	£4
portraits	£2

See also silks

Human butterflies	£8-£15
Tuck, Aesop's Fables	£8

World War II

Cartoons £6-£10
see National Socialist Party

Leaders and personalities

Cabinet ministers	£2
Candidates	£8+
Churchill	£6-£20
Governor Generals	£3-£5
Lloyd George	£2-£3
Prime Ministers	£2
Tuck political postcards, early	£15-£25

Artists

Bradshaw, P.V.B	£6
Corbella, T.	£6
Furniss, Harry	£5-£8
Hansi	£12-£15
Hardy, Dudley	£6
Longmire, R.O.	£8-£12
Ludovici, A.	£4
Martini	£20-£30
Moreland, Arthur	£6-£10
Orens, Denizard	£15-£25
Raemaeker, Louis	£2
Rostro	£12-£15
Spy, Ward L. (Vanity Fair)	£20

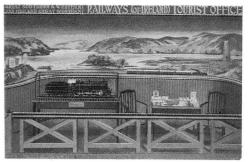

Published for the Festival of Empire, 1924. £30

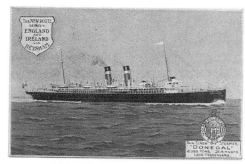

Midland Railway's Donegal. £8

LNER view card. £12

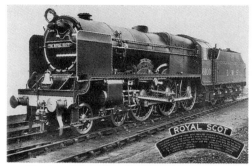

Kitted out for its trip to the USA. The Royal Scot.
Better so £6

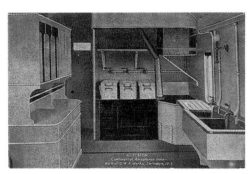

GWR ambulance train, 1915. The 1916 train is better. £3.50

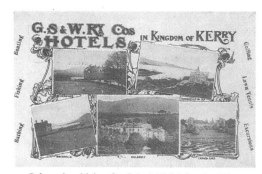

Coloured multiview for G.S. & W.R.'s hotels. £25

North Eastern Railway panoramic card. £20

North Staffordshire Railway view of the
Leek & Manifold line. £6

Although the number of collectors seems to be diminishing, there is still plenty of demand for unusual and unique cards. The price trend is ever upwards for this type of material. *No matter how this section is written and priced, there are always cards that fall outside the broad prices given.*

OFFICIAL CARDS

Barry Railway
Barry Docks, correspondence	£35
Barry Island, coloured view	£30
Paddle steamers, lithographic	£10
tinted	£15

Belfast and County Down Railway
Hotels, b&w	£8-£15
Ships	£12
Slieve Donard Hotel (Jotter)	£10

Bideford, Westward Ho!, and Appledore Railway
	£25

British Rail
Maps, cross channel services	£15+
Ships and trains, hotels	£3-£6

Caledonian and London & North Western Railway
Royal mail route coloured/b&w	£15
Sleeping car with plan	£50
West Coast Joint Stock	£10-£15

Caledonian Railway
Engines/rolling stock, coloured	£4-£8
b&w Glosso views	£8
Hotel posters	£10-£20
Hotels	£4+
interiors, b&w	£6
interiors, coloured	£8
Posters, photographic/coloured	£60-£80
Reliable series steamers/views	£10-£15
Tartan border views	£8
Views,	
green or brown artwork, 1903	£25
coloured	£6-£12
Vignette card, pictures both sides	£25

Callander & Oban Railway
Ballachulish Hotel	£20

Sepia views (from booklet) £20

Cambrian Railways
Maps	£35
Views, Valentines	£6-£8
Photochrom	£6-£8
others	£10
correspondence	£15
Vignettes	£25

Campbeltown and Machrihanish Light Railway
Poster	£100

Central London Railway
1911 Strike	£40
Celesque series	£12
Novelties	£40-£75
Picture and route map	£25
Posters	£35

Cheshire Lines Committee
Correspondence	£40

Cork, Bandon & South Coast Railway
Oilette (Sunnyside of Ireland)	£3

Cork, Blackrock & Passage Railway
Paddle Steamer 'Audrey'	£35

Corris Railway
Corris Railway series	£8
Printed views	£12
Views, photographic	£4-£6

District Railway
Court size	£40

Dublin & South Eastern Railway
Views, correspondence	£30
Hotel Jotter	£10

RAILWAY

Dublin, Wicklow & Wexford Railway
View, undivided back   £35

Dumbarton & Balloch Joint Lines Committee
Ships   £15
Views, b&w   £12
    coloured   £15

East Coast Route
Andrew Reid vignette   £15
Rolling stock and views   £5-£12

Festiniog Railway
Anonymous sepia
    photographic views   £10
Photochrom photographic views   £8+
Poster, Switzerland of Wales   £75

Freshwater, Yarmouth & Newport Railway
Vignettes   £35

Furness Railway
Barrow and Fleetwood steamers
    (Series 20)   £15
Engines and rolling stock
    (Series 18-19)   £6+
Exhibitions   £45
Furness Abbey (series 14-15)   £2
Furness Abbey Hotel (series 16-17) £6
G. Romney paintings,
    (series 12-13)   £20
Lakes steamers (series 9-11)   £5
McCorquodale, vignette   £35-£40
    views   £3+
Photographic views, HHH series   £20
Posters (Series 21)   £80+
Sankey Tours through Lakeland   £20
Tuck views (series 1-7)   £3.50
Tuck views (series 8)   £5

Glasgow & South Western Railway
Hotels   £4
Hotels, multi-view   £5
McCorquodale, steamers,   £3
Oilettes   £4
Posters   £60+
Vignette views   £20-£25
Other   £8+

Great Central Railway
Faulkner views,
    as panel greeting cards   £12
    photographic HHH series   £20
    series 545 and 546   £12
Immingham docks   £4
Poster   £60
Shipping (Turner, C.E.)   £12-£15
    printed   £10
    photographic   £12
    steam ship department   £40
    Tuck   £35
Shipping co. cards, overprinted   £20-30
Vignettes   £35

Great Eastern Railway
Correspondence cards   £30
    Oilette (on front)   £30
    Jarrold   £40
Faulkner, cathedrals with crest   £75
Faulkner (series 118)   £80
'Greetings from Harwich'
    vignettes   £8-£12
Hotels   £4-£8
Posters   £80+
Ships, coloured   £8-£12
    b&w   £6-£10
Tuck, vignettes   £80
Views, with crest on picture   £2.50

Great Northern & City Railway
Posters, b&w   £50
Views   £8

Great Northern, Piccadilly & Brompton Railway
Locomotive Publishing Co.   £6-£10
Map   £25

Great Northern Railway
Locomotive Publishing Co   £15
Photochrom views, engines,
    b&w   £40
    coloured   £2-6
    correspondence   £30
Posters   £80
Skegness &
    Sheringham panoramas   £60

Vignettes, views	£35
hotels	£8-15

Great Northern Railway (Ireland)

Hotels, multi-view	£15
others	£10
Mulroy Bay Bus	£40
Views, correspondence	£15

Great North of Scotland Railway

Cruden Bay golf tournament	£40
Hotel, multi-view	£25
Hotel, multi-view	
with pictures on both sides	£30
Palace Hotel series	£15
Porter, Aberdeen views	£25

Great Southern Railway

Hotels, sepia photos	£5
others	£8

Great Southern & Western Railway

Great Southern Hotel, coloured	£5
Hotels, multi-view	£25
Lawrence views	£10
Joint with M.G.W.	
(Wembley 1924)	£30
Jotter	£6
Oilette (Sunnyside of Ireland)	£3
Panorama, correspondence	£60
Parknasilla Poster,	
correspondence	£60

Great Western Railway

Correspondence, various types	£25+
Wyndham	£25+
Engines (series 6)	£2
others	£2-3
Hotel vignettes	£15+
other	£3+
Posters (series 3)	£80
others	£40+
Shipping, coloured	£15
photographic	£4
Views, coloured	£3-6
GWR crest by picture	£40
sepia	£3-10
vignette	£35

Hampstead Tube

Last Link coloured views	£6·
Multi-views, map on back	£12

Highland Railway

Coloured	£15
Early coloured views,	
red circular crest	£25
Hotels, Inverness	£5
Map, correspondence	£75
Photos, on the Highland Railway	£15
Views, straight line inscription	£20
circular crest	£20
Others	£8-£12

Hull & Barnsley Railway

Scenes at Alexandra Dock, etc.	£35
Views	£35

Invergarry & Fort Augustus Railway

Views, Highland Railway Series	£30

Isle of Wight Central Railway

Views	£35
Vignettes	£35

Isle of Wight Railway

Vignettes	£35

Joint South Western & Brighton Railway

Vignettes	£35

Kent & East Sussex Railway

Engine, correspondence	£10
Other correspondence issues	£30
Views, numbered 1-6	£8

Lancashire & Yorkshire Railway

Correspondence	£25
Engines	£2+
overprinted, French	£6
Posters	£75
Ships (1907 series)	£4
new series	£6
overprinted French, all series	£6
Views (1905 and 1907 series)	£2.50
new series	£4
overprinted French, all series	£6
Vignettes	£25+

RAILWAY

Liverpool Overhead Railway
Dock views £25

London & North Eastern Railway
Camping coaches £10-£15
Hotels, York and Newcastle £2
    others £3-£12
Northern Belle Cruise, unused £25
   used, with cachet £75
Posters £80
Ships £5-£12
Trains £2-£4
Views £6-£12

London & North Western Railway
McCorquodale
   buses, lorries, etc. £8-£12
   engines, views, ships £2-£4
   exhibitions £20+
   posters £40-£75
   hotels £3-£4
   maps, correspondence £75
   views, correspondence £2
St. Louis Exposition,
   undivided back £8-£18
Tuck
   engines, views, ships, etc. £2-£4
   colour, royal trains, etc. £2-£4
   Hotels £3-£5

London & South Western Railway
Correspondence, view with crest £45
Hotel poster £60
Orphanage £6
Orphanage collecting day £10
Posters £75+
Ships, coloured, early £20-£25
   b&w £4-£6
Vignettes, coloured £30+
   b&w £25

London, Brighton & South Coast Railway
Correspondence £40
French vignettes, red overprint £20
Posters £80-£100
Vignettes £25
Waterlow, views (series 1,2,4) £2.50
   bridges (series 3) £4

(series 6) £4

London, Chatham & Dover Railway
Vignettes, coloured £35
   b&w £25

Londonderry & Lough Swilly Railway
Map, correspondence £60

London, Midland & Scottish Railway
Camping coaches £15
Gleneagle Golf, coloured £75
Hotels £3-£8
Ships £6
Road vehicles, removals £35
Trains and engines £2-£4
Views with 'handwritten' message £15

Lynton & Barnstaple Railway
Stations and views (Peacock) £20+

Maryport & Carlisle Railway
Map, correspondence £100

Metropolitan District Railway
Photographic Locos
   & Rolling Stock £6

Metropolitan Railway
Maps £15
Posters £60+
Views, b&w £15
   sepia (numbered 1-30) £6+

Midland & Great Northern Joint Railway
Views, correspondence £35

Midland Great Western Railway
Hotels £8

Midland (Northern Counties Committee)
Hotels £6
Trains £15
Views, correspondence £35

Midland Railway
Carriages £12
Engines £2
Hotels, coloured vignettes £3-£5+

b&w or sepia vignettes	£25
others	£3-£5
Maps	£15-£25
Midland Express/St. Pancras	£30
Photochrom views	£2-£4
others	£6
Posters	£60+
Ships	£5-£8
Vignettes, b&w	£20+
coloured, Andrew Reid	£20

Newport, Godshill & St. Lawrence Railway

Vignettes	£35

North British Railway

Views and ship's crest on front	£12-£15
b&w and coloured	£8-£12
Caledonia (129),	
North British Railway Series	£2
Scottish Exhibition	
poster overprint	£60
Ships, coloured	£8
Hotels	£2-£4

North Eastern Railway

Brussels Exhibition	£15
Hotels, York & Newcastle	£2-£4
other	£3-£12
Hull Riverside quay	£4
Photographic panoramic views	
numbers 1-40	£20
with maps below picture	£30
Posters	£60-£75
Ships	£4-£6

North Staffordshire Railway

Correspondence	£15
Golf & glossy anonymous views	£15
McCorquodale and W&K views	£3-£10
White border views, W&K	
and W&TG	£10

Portpatrick & Wigontownshire Joint Railway

Views	£35+
Ships	£15-£20

Snowdon Mountain Railway

Court card	£60

posters	£40-£60
Other issues	£3-£4
Snowdon series, Nos. 1-90	£8-£12

Somerset & Dorset Joint Railway

Views, correspondence	£45

South Eastern and Chatham (& Dover) Railway

Correspondence	£30
Hotels	£8
London-Paris, English or French	£12
McCorquodale, views, etc.	£2+
Maps	£20
Posters	£100
Vignettes, blue frame, etc.	£35
sepia	£25

Southern Railway

Leonard Richmond paintings	£25
Posters	£80
Ships	£3-£10
ship's name in large letters	£60
correspondence	£60
hotels	£6
Small picture posters	£60

Stratford-on-Avon & Midland Junction Railway

Poster	£100

Underground

Posters	
London Nooks and Corners	£45
others	£25-£50
W.H.S.	£12

Vale of Rheidol Railway

Views, advertising overprints	£15-£20

West Clare Railway

Views	£25

West Highland Railway

Views, on the West Highland Railway	
	£6

RAILWAY

Weston, Clevedon &
Portishead Light Railway
Trains, photographic   £40

Wick & Lybster Light Railway
Views (Highland Railway Series) £30

Wirral Railway
Map, correspondence   £100
Views, correspondence   £50

Others
French Posters
  artist signed   £10
  Orleans post 1920   £10
  UB Chromo-Litho   £25

Official issues, overprinted on the reverse for
correspondence use, command a premium over
normal issues. The correspondence cards
listed above were printed specifically for that
purpose, and were not sold to the public.

NON-OFFICIAL ISSUES

TRAINS AND ENGINES

Anonymous
  24 Glossy cards   £4
Birn Bros., series G56   £2.50
Caledonia   £3
H.M. & Co, Express of the World £5
Hartmann railway series 3061   £5
Hellier's locomotive series   £2
High Level series
  (Hills, Sunderland)   £4
Homewood (Stations)   £20+
JWB Commercial series 312   £1
Knight series   £1.50
LCC reward cards   £2.50
Locomotive Magazine series
  (L.P. Co.)   £1.50+
Locomotive Publishing Co
  court card (F. Moore)   £30
  vignettes, coloured   £30
  vignettes, monochrome   £20
  coloured   £1.50-£4
  b&w   £1.50-£3
  photographic   £1.50

Photochrom   £1.50
Pouteau
  coloured   £1.50
  b&w   £2
  photographic   £1.50
MB series 208-213, greetings   £1.50
McCorquodale, Vulcan Foundry £6
Mack W.E., coloured   £3
  photographic style   £1
Misch & Stock series 331 & 332   £4
Monarch (R Johnston, Gateshead)£4
Railway Magazine series   £1.50
R.S. Art Press   £1.50
Russells   £3
Salmon   £2
Scott, Russell   £2
Series 1923, birthday greetings   £3
Speedwell   £4
Spree, Hastings Express   £8
Tuck
  series 5303, 5304   £5
  other series   £3.50
  London stations   £8
Valentine
  Irish set   £12
  London stations   £6
  other coloured   £1.50-£2.50
  photographic style   £1.50
Wildt &Kray Series 1814 & 1834£1.50
  photographic style   £1.50
Wrench
  Red Border   £4
  Electric railways   £4+
  Other b&w   £1.50
  Other pre-1950 issues   £1

Miscellaneous
Accidents and disasters   £8-£25
Bridges, viaducts, and tunnels   £1-£4
Gothard multi-view cards   £15-£25
Level crossings   £3-£6
Lifts, cliff etc.   £1.50
Miniature   £3-£8
Motor buses, close up   £15-£60
Mountain railways   £2-£4
Narrow gauge   £4-£20
Permanent way   £1.50
Romney, Hythe & Dymchurch
  Railway views   £2-£4

Laurel and Hardy on £25

For railway stations see Topographical.

Artists

Fleury, H.	£2.50-£6
Moore, F.	75p+
Parsons, F.J.	£1+

An NBR 0-6-0. £1.50

From Tuck 'Famous Expresses' series IX. £3.50

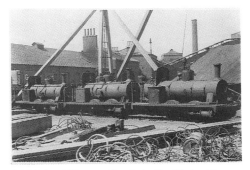

0-4-0 industrial locos at Dawsholm Gas Works, Glasgow.
£8 maybe

French Railway posters. Very attractive but slow moving.

Prince Edward. £5
                Just one of the many Indian Maharajahs. £4

Russian royalty is the best. £15

Continues to sell steadily with noticeably more interest in Foreign royalty.

BRITISH

Queen Victoria

Diamond Jubilee 1897, unused	£75-£125
used in 1897	£150+
Family groups	£5-£8
Mourning cards	£15-£20
Portraits	£8-£15
Tuck, early	£15-£25

Edward VII

Coronation souvenir 1902	£10-£15
procession, 1902	£1.50
H. Cassiers, London	
views series	£6
Funeral procession, 1910	£1-£2
Mourning card, 1910	£3
Portraits and family groups	£1.50-£3
Royal Tour	
Prince and Princess of Wales	£15-£25
set postally used at all stops	£300
Visits, British	£10-£15
overseas	£6-£25

George V

Coronation procession, 1911	£1
Coronation souvenir, 1911	£4-£6
Delhi Durbar	£3-£6
Investiture of Prince of Wales	£4
Mourning cards, 1936	£3
Portraits and family groups	£2-£3
Silver Jubilee procession, 1935	£1
Silver Jubilee souvenir, 1935	£4-£6
Visits, British	£10-£15
overseas	£6-£15

Edward VIII

Coronation souvenir	£5
Portraits	£4-£6
Visits, local, 1936	£12-£15
overseas	£8-£15
Wedding souvenir	£25
with Mrs Simpson	£25-£35

George VI

Coronation, 1937	£3-£5
procession	£1
Mourning cards, 1952	£5
Portraits and family groups	£2-£4
Victory celebrations, 1945	£1
Visits, local and foreign	£8-£15

Elizabeth II

Children	£1.50-£3
Coronation, 1953	£2-£4
procession/ceremony	£1
Engagement	£2-£3
Investiture of Prince of Wales	£2-£3
Overseas visits, early	£4-£6
Portraits, photographic, b&w	£1.50-£2.50
coloured	£2-£3
others	50p-£2
Queen Mother's 80th birthday	50p
Silver Jubilee souvenir	50p
Visits, local, 1953	£6-£8
Wedding souvenir	£4-£6

Prince and Princess of Wales

Children	25p
Engagement	25p-50p
Other portraits	50p-£2
Wedding	50p

Miscellaneous

Gatherings	£2-£4
Kings and Queens, Tuck series	£12
Faulkner's series	£8
King Insurance Co.	£6
Royal weddings	£3-£6

FOREIGN

Portraits

Commemoratives	£10-£20
East European	£4-£6
Embossed souvenir cards	£15-£20
Others	£3-£8
Russian, British publishers	£8-£15
cartoons	£15-£25
continental publishers	£15-£25
Weddings	£5-£8

A rare early shipping advert. £25

Published by Carpenter of Ramsgate, this is the first launch of the new lifeboat. £20

Shipping continues to sell extremely well, with a great demand for the nice coloured cards, particularly posters and early artist types. Naval is also in demand, particularly wooden-walled ships and those elusive (to the seeker), photographic warships.

MERCHANT

Advertising (Officials)

Poster type	£25-£40
Publicity type vignettes	£15-£25
Other early issues	£10-£25
Later, coloured	£6-£12
b&w	£4-£8

Liners, etc.

Interiors	£3-£8
Japanese	£10-£15
Launchings	£15
'Lusitania'	£8
in memoriam cards	£10-£15
'Titanic', photographic	
actual	£30-£80
'Olympic'	£20-£40
in memoriam cards	£30-£60
art type	£20-£40
associated ships:	
'Olympic', 'Carpathia', etc.	£8-£40
Tuck, Oilettes	£8
Other liners (pre-1939), coloured	£5-£10
b&w	£3-£6
photographic	£3-£6
Other liners (post-war)	£2-£5

Miscellaneous

Cargo boats	£3-£4
Coastal vessels	£3-£6
Docks/harbours	£4-£8
exceptional real photographic	
views	£10-£20
construction	£15-£25
Ferries, river	£1-£3
cross Channel	£4-£8
Belgian postal stationery	£6-10
Hospital ships	£10-£20
Lifeboats	
photographic	£10-£25
printed	£6-£15
crews	£5-£10
parades	£20-£35
'inland launchings'	£25-£40

coastguard/stations	£1.50-£2.50
advertising posters, R.N.L.I.	£25
Lighthouses	£1-£5
Lightships	£6-£8
Paddle steamers, close-up	£5-£20
wrecks	£20-£30
Foreign paddle steamers	
Rhine steamers	£3-£8
Swiss lake steamers	£2-£4
others	£1-£2
Pleasure boats, identified	£1.50-£5
Royal Yacht, 'Victoria & Albert'	£3
Sailing barges, photographic	£6-£20
printed	£3-£8
Sailing ships, photographic	
square riggers, etc.	£4-£6
Ship building and yards	£4-£12
Trawlers	£3-£6
Tugs, etc.	£4
Wrecks	
photographic	£10-£20
printed	£5-£10
Yachts	£1-£2

NAVAL

Fighting Vessels

British photographic type	£3-£5
launchings	£6
aircraft carriers	£5-£8
submarines	£5-£8
other vessels	£3-£5
Foreign photographic type	£3-£5
submarines	£5-£8

Many photographic cards were produced after WW2, usually with plain backs and are worth slightly less than earlier issues.

Art Types

Tuck 'Empire'	£20
Oilette	£4
British, general	£2-£4
Foreign, early	£2-£4
Japanese commemorative	£6-£10
other vessels	£2-£4

SHIPPING

Miscellaneous

Life in the Navy	
Oilette	£3+
others	£2
Nelson	
HMS Victory, etc.	£1-£2
Oilette	£4+
Trafalgar day souvenir, 1905	£6+
others	£2-£4
Transport/troopships	£4-£6
Wooden walled ships	£4-£8

CUNARD LINE R.M.S. "CARINTHIA"
TONNAGE 20,000. LENGTH 624 FEET. BREADTH 74 FEET.

An Odin Rosenvinge painting for Cunard. £3.50

ARTISTS

Bannister, A.F.D.	£4
Black, Algernon	£8
Black, Montague B.	£8
Burgess, Arthur	£5
Cassiers, H.	£10-£15
Church, Bernard W.	£4
Cumming, Neville	£5
Dixon, Charles	£6
Edler, Eduard	£8
Freer, H.B.	£5
Fry, John H.	£6
Gabriel, E.	£8
Hamilton, E.	£4-£6
Hardy, Dudley J.	£8-£10
Lacy, Chas de	£8
Lessieux, E. Louis	£15-£30
Mann, James S.	£8
Montague, R.	£4
Praga, Alfred	£6-£10
Rooke, H.K.	£6
Rosenvinge, Odin	£8
Shoesmith, Kenneth	£8
Stower, Willi	
early	£10-£15
later	£4
Thomas, Walter	£6
Turner, C.E.	£5
Ullman, Max	£10
Wilkinson, Norman	£6
Wyllie, W.L.	£6

Red Star Line. Antwerp-Dover-New York
Twin Screw Mailsteamer "FINLAND"

The Red Star line sailed from Antwerp. £15

As usual, good quality and unusual designs sell, whether woven or embroidered. Rare regimental badges find a ready market.

WOVEN, FRENCH

A. Benoiston/Paris Exposition

1900	£100
Others	£30-£40

Neyret Freres

1903/4 1905/14	£40-£200
1907-1918	£25-£60
WW 1 patriotics, portraits, etc.	£20-£50
Flames	£20-£60
Greetings	£20-£35

Other Types

Bertrand and Boiron	£40+
Others	£15-£40

GERMAN

H.M. Kreiger	£25-£60
Rudolf Knuffman	£25-£60
Nazi Interest/1936-1938	£40+
Others	£20-£60

OTHER EUROPEAN

Early	£25-£50
Later	£20-£40

JAPANESE

Views and portraits	£20-£40
With copy of Grand Mount	£40

U.S.A.

1904 exposition	£150
Set of 14	£2500
Others	£25-£65

GRANT W.H.

Exhibitions	£40-£80
Portraits/royalty	£35-£80
Subjects	£30-£75

Hands Across the Sea/

ships and greetings	£30-£60
Greetings from	£25-£50
Greetings, songs and hymns	£30-£45
Views	£20-£50

STEVENS T.

Experimental types	£80
Portraits	£50-£200
Religious subjects	£35-£50
Views	£25-£150
General subjects	£25-£135

Ships

Titanic	£750
Battleships	£75-£150
Transports	£40-£60
Liners, steamers and landing stages	£35-£60
Hands Across the Sea	£25-£60

Alpha Series
(Designs produced by Stevens for Alpha Publishing Co.)

Greetings	£20-£30
Flags	£25-£45
Stevens designs	£30-£60

PRINTED SILK/SATIN

Flames/Edition Gabriel	£15-£25
Kitchener, Lord	£15
Stewart & Woolfe series	£10
Regiments/countries	£8
Tuck greetings	£6
Cinema stars, plain backs	£3
Miscellaneous	£3

H.M. Krieger

Four seasons set	£200
Others	£20-£25

Cavell, Edith

In original D.M. envelope	£8
Card only	£6

SILKS

All Royal Marine silks are well collected. £40

Complete with insert. £8

Christmas greetings. £8

Russian royalty on a 1915 silk. £25

Tobogganing. A rare design. £15

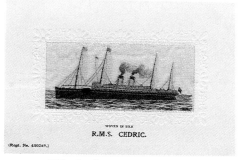

White Star liner RMS Cedric. £45

FAB PATCHWORK CARDS

W.N. Sharpe/Bradford

Actresses	£15
Royalty	£20
Views	£12-£15
Heraldic	£10
Flowers	£8
PAT.735 (Gaunt Armley)	£10

Embroidered

Early (Pre 1910)	£6-£15

Year Dates

1914-1919	£6
1920-1923	£8
1925-1939	£8-£12
1940	£4
1945	£8

Heraldic

British towns/counties	£15-£25
European towns/countries	£8-£10
Other overseas	£20-£60

Personalitites

Inset photos, single	£8-£15
Inset photos, doubles	£10-£25
Names - WWI leaders	£15-£20
Saints and personal names	£6

Regimental

Overseas regiments	£30-£60
Royal Navy, etc.	£8-£10
Royal Navy ships	£30-£45
Royal Naval Air Service	£25-£35
Royal Navy units, inc. Marines	£15-£35
Line regiments	£25-£50
Corps (A.S.C., R.E., R.F.A., etc)	£10-£15
Army camps	£15-£25
Red Cross, Y.M.C.A., Salvation Army, etc.	£20-£30
Royal Air Force/R.F.C.	£20-£30

Better Designs

Advertising	£35
Aircraft/guns, etc.	£8-£12
Buildings	£10-£20
Buildings, war destruction	£10-£15
Cartoons	£10+
Cathedrals in flames	£10-£15
Cats	£8-£12
Exhibitions	£25-£35
Father Christmas	£15-£20
Soldiers/sailors/medals, etc	£8-£12
Zeppelins	£8-£15

Others

Patriotic/flags	£5-£8
Floral and sentimental	£5-£8

Many cards of this type were made in the form of an envelope. If such a card still contains its original insert, the following premium may be added to the prices above:

Inserts

Silk handkerchief	£6
Artist, signed	£2
Celluloid	£4
War scenes	£2
Perfumed	£1

MACHINE EMBROIDERED

Birn Bros.

Embossed regimental badges	£15+
Embossed cards with silk inserts	£5+

Tuck R. & Sons
Broderie D'Art series

Spanish Embroidery

Early cards	£6
Later/modern	£2

Published by W.H. Grant of Coventry. £60

The police were drafted in from elsewhere during strikes, even in 1910. £35

Fishing with keddle nets at Camber, Sussex. £25

This section includes some of the finest topographical cards as well as collected themes such as lacemaking, postal, and scouting, all of which sell well when they can be found.

FISHING INDUSTRY

Fishermen	£3-£6
mending nets	£3-£8
Fisherwomen, identified locality	£5-£10
Trawlers	£3-£6
dockside views	£5-£20
Hull trawler outrage	£3-£5

FOLKLORE

County humour/sayings	£1-£2
Dunmow Flitch	£3-£6
Ducking stools, gibbets, etc.	50p-£1
Ghosts	75p
Gretna Green	50p
Lady Godiva	£3-£8
Legends	£1-£2
Morris dancers	£15-£35

LONDON LIFE

Celesque Series	£4-£8
Cries of London (Rotophot)	£2
Kyd	£8
Rotary series	£10-£50
Sauber	£6
Tuck, R., early	£8
Oilette	£3-£6
Wyndham series	£15-£30
Other series	£1-£5

MEDICAL

Hospitals	£4-£6
Hospital wards	£3-£6
identified	£4-£6
Nurses	£2+
Operating theatres	£6
Red Cross postcards	£3-£8+
St. John's Ambulance	£3+
T.B. fund raising	£3+
Lincoln typhoid outbreak	£35-£60
Dentistry	
surgeries	£4-£6
comics	£6-£8

POLICE

Policemen, single	£3
groups	£3
comic	£3-£6
Harry Payne	£25-£30

POSTAL

Language of stamps	£2-£3
Postmen, unidentified	£2-£5
Postwomen, unidentified	£3-£5
Postmen of the World	£10+
Some have been reproduced	
Postmen of the British Empire	£12
Comic	£3-£6
Fuller, Edmund G.	£6
Postmen, etc., novelty pull-out	£4-£6
Post boxes, etc	£3-£5
Telegram representations	£2-£4

RELIGION

Church Army	£1.50
Clergymen	50p
at named locations	£2-£4
Evangelists	£2-£4
vans	£15-£25
Jewish greetings	£1-£4
Lord's Prayer per card	£2-£5
Oberammergau passion plays	75p-£2
Roman Catholicism	50p-£2
events/processions	£3-£8
Salvation Army	£2-£4
General Booth (portraits)	£2-£4
Visits to locations	£8-£12
others	£2-£4
Synagogues	
British	£12-£35
foreign	£10-£50
Missionary societies	£1-£3

Overseas cards can be worth more.

SOCIAL HISTORY

A Tom Browne dentistry comic. £10

OPENING OF SALVATION ARMY CITADEL, OXFORD II.,
By BRIGADIER ROBERTS, 2nd November, 1905.

They opened just in time for Christmas, 1905. £15

Frank Ball scouting comic published by Tuck. £8

A Rotary series London Life card.
Covent Garden doesn't look like this anymore. £20

A boy scout guard of honour at Ventnor on
the Isle of Wight, 1911. £10

Some of the staff of a Glasgow branch of the S.C.W.S. £8

RURAL LIFE

Blacksmiths, identified locality	
photographic	£15-£40
printed	£3-£12
Bootmakers	
photographic	£15-£25
printed	£10+
Children at play	
photographic	£3-£8
printed	£3-£5
Cliff climbers	
photographic	£4-£6
printed	£2-£4
Coopers	
photographic	£15-£25
printed	£10
Coracle fishermen	
photographic	£3-£8
printed	£2
Crofters	
photographic	£5-£8
printed	£2-£6
Dalesmen	£1.50
Deer Stalking	£1.50
Evictions	
photographic	£40-£75
printed	£25-£40
Farmworkers	
photographic	£4-£10
printed	£2-£6
Flower farming and picking	
photographic	£4-£10
printed	£2-£6
Fruit picking	
photographic	£6-£8
printed	£3-£6
Gipsy camps, identified locality	
photographic	£25-£40
printed	£15-£25
Gipsies on the road, identified locality	
photographic	£20-£35
printed	£15-£25
Unidentified cards are worth about 25%-50% less	
Harvesting	
photographic	£6-£12
printed	£4-£8
Harvesting with machinery	
photographic	£10-£20

printed	£6-£10
Herdsmen	
photographic	£2-£4
printed	£1-£3
Hermits	
photographic	£8-£15
printed	£2-£8
Hop picking	
photographic	£8-£20
printed	£4-£6
Hunting/shooting	
photographic	£2-£6
printed	£2-£6
Knitting	
photographic	£3-£6
printed	£3-£5
Lace making, English handworkers	
photographic	£15-£35
printed	£6-£20
Lace making, factory scenes	
photographic	£4-£6
printed	£4-£6
Lace making, named lacemakers	
photographic	£20-£40
printed	£15-£25
Lace making, Belgian	£4-£10
Lace making , French	£8-£15
Lace making, Ceylon, Malta, etc.	£4-£8
Lambing	
photographic	£1-£3
printed	£1-£2
Lavender fields, identified locality	
photographic	£4-£6
printed	£3-£6
May Day celebrations, identified locality	
photographic	£15-£25
printed	£10-£15
National dress, Irish	£1.50
National dress, Welsh	
photographic	£2-£3
printed	£1.50+
Ox carts	
photographic	£8-£15
printed	£6-£8
Peat digging	
photographic	£2-£5
printed	£1-£2

SOCIAL HISTORY

Performing bears, identified locality	
photographic	£60
printed	£25-£35
Performing bears, overseas	£8-£15
Ploughing	
photographic	£6-£10
printed	£3-£8
Reaping	
photographic	£3-£6
printed	£1-£2
Roasts	
photographic	£15-£20
printed	£8-£12
Sheep shearing and dipping	
photographic	£6-£10
printed	£2-£6
Spinning and weaving	
photographic	£2-£6
printed	£2-£3
Stocks, ducking stools, etc.	50p-£1
Village crafts	
photographic	£5-£10
printed	£2-£6
Village folk	
photographic	£4-£8
printed	£2-£4
Village life, including Oilettes	£2-£4
Water carriers	
photographic	£10-£25
printed	£8-£15
Well dressing	
photographic	£4-£6
printed	£2-£4
Wheelwrights	
photographic	£15-£25
printed	£5-£10

As many of these cards are possibly one-off examples, this list is only intended as a guide to pricing for some of the better-known types.

YOUTH ORGANISATIONS

Scouts	
Baden-Powell portraits	£15-£25
at functions	£20-£25
military cards	£15+
Relief of Mafeking	£25
Comic	£8+
Groups	

identified troupes	£8-£12
unidentified troupes	£2
events and activities	£8-£15
International jamborees	£10-£25
Personalities	£6-£10
Jack Cornwell, VC	£8-£12
Tuck, Harry Payne	£25-£30
animal heads	£100

Boys Brigade	£12

Girl Guides	
Lady Baden-Powell	£8+
Princess Royal (Mary)	£4
Princess Elizabeth	£4
other leaders	£2-£4
Camp sites	
official cards	£3
groups	£2-£4

Other youth organizations	£2-£6

Special postmarks add considerably to the value.

Granny Nairn of Newburgh, Fife, aged 100 years. £5

There is no sign of collecting in this area slowing down. If you have the cards you can sell them! For the old favourites, cricket, professional football and professional golf the sky's the limit. Ping pong and stadia are all selling exceedingly well.

Angling	£2-£6
Comic	£2-£4
Archery	£3
Athletics	
Known athletes	£3-£6
Meetings	£6-£8
Olympic games	£6-£35
Stadia	£4-£6
Billiards/Snooker	
Comic	£5-£8
Players (named)	£10-£15
Rooms/playing	£3-£6
Cricket	
Comic	£5-£10
Kinsella	£6
Grounds	£5-£8
Players	£12-£15
signed	£15-£40
Posters	£40
Teams	£12-£15
international	£12-£15
Star series	£6
Football	
Amateur grounds	£5-£8
Amateur Teams, identified	£5-£10
armed services	£2
Comic	£4-£6+
Kinsella	£6
Commemorative cards	£25
Crowd scenes	£6
Memoriam cards	£25
Poster adverts, teams	£40+
Professional players/teams	£20-£30
Golf	
Comic	£8-£15
Competitions	£25-£35
Courses	£6-£10
Players, named	£30-£40

Poster adverts	£40-£75
Product adverts	£15-£35
Horse Jumping	
Riders	£3-£5
Show advertising	£6-£10
Horse Racing	
Courses and buildings	£4-£8
Gatwick	£25
Jockeys	£4-£6
Race horses, coloured	£3-£6
b&w	£3-£4
Hunting	
Art	£2-£4
Photographic, named	£5-£10
Mountaineering	
Everest	£8-£12
Miscellaneous	£2-£4
Olympics	£6-£35
Rowing (named)	£4-£8
Rugby, players and teams	£6-£8
Shooting	
Bisley	£6-£10
Other locations	£3-£8
Speedway	
Riders, pre-war	£8+
Post-war	£6+
Swimming	
Channel	£4-£6
Other	£4-£6

SPORT

Joe Beckett. £8

The touring side of 1935. £8

Opening of Salcombe R.F.C.'s new ground. £20

John Beere famous racehorse published by Max Ettlinger. £5

A rugby comic published by Miller & Lang of Glasgow. £2.50

The Argentinian team for the 1924 Paris Olympics. £20

Table Tennis

Comic	£10-£15
Early	£25
People playing	£5
Players	£12-£15

Tennis

Courts	£3-£5
Kinsella	£6
Players	£6+
Post-war, 1950s	£4+

Walking

Road, identified	£4-£8

Winter Sports

	£2-£4
Pelligrini	£12-£15
Other art types	£3-£8

Wrestling and Body Building	£4-£8

Artists

Becker, C.	£10
Bird, H.	£2.50
Crombie, C.M.	£15
Dink	£4
Eliott, Harry	£15
Koch, Ludwig	£4
Lehmann, Felix	£4
Mason, Finch	£3

4201 — LAWN TENNIS

Italian Art Deco tennis caricature. £10

THE BELLE OF THE BALL.

From Davidson series 2525-6.
Golf comics are good sellers. £12

GEO. PATERSON, WRESTLER.
Holder of 13 Stone and Heavy-Middle Weight Championships.

George Paterson, Scottish wrestler. £8

If you went down to the woods at Haywards Heath in 1911 you'd have been able to join the picnic. £30

Cresswell Colliery, Derbyshire. £25

AVIATION

Airships
Local flights	£30-£40
Named	£8-£15
Zeppelins, military	£3-£6
World flights	£10-£20

Art Types
Tuck, etc.	£4-£6
Salmon, etc.	£3-£5

Balloons
Local British flights	
photographic	£20-£40
printed	£8-£25
Military flights, printed	£2-£6
Swiss, meeting posters	£60+

Early
Brooklands	£12
Daily Mail Tour 1912	£8
named locations	£20-£30
Flying at Hendon	£6
International flights	£15-£25
Meetings	£15-£25
posters	£30+
Military	£4
Named accidents	£25-£30
Named locations	£25-£30
Unidentified	£6-£8

Imperial Airways
Official cards	£8+
Pilots	£12

Later Aviation
Pre-war identified airlines	£4-£8
Joy flights	£4-£6
W.W.II	£1.50-£4
Post-war (officials)	£2-£6

Miscellaneous
Airfields	£6-£10
Croydon	£8-£12
French	£6-£15
Comic	£2.50-£4
R.F.C. interest	£3+

BICYCLES
Advertising	£15-£35
Close-up photographic	£4-£6
Comic	£3-£5
Military	£4-£6
Racing, pre-war	£6-£12
post-war	£4-£10
Tandems	£8
Tricycles	£8-£12

BUSES
Horse, close-up, photographic	£45-£65
printed	£8-£20
Motor, close-up, photographic	£25-£75
printed	£20-£40

There are many printed cards, often of London, some of poor quality, worth about £6

CANALS
Boats and barges, close-up	£30-£75
Construction and cleaning	£30-£40
Disasters	£30-£60
General views	£6-£20
Locks, bridges and aqueducts	£5-£12
Military canals	£2+
People, events, gatherings, etc.	£30-£60
Ship canals	£2-£6
Tunnels	£4-£8

CHARABANCS
Identified	£3-£6

COACHES (HORSE-DRAWN)
Art type	£3-£6
Early	£25
Mail Coaches	£8-£25
art type	£4+
Maggs	£2
overseas	£3-£6
Named locations	£15-£35
Photographic	£4-£8

Balloonists at the Shrewsbury Flower Show. £15

R. Bett and his van at 44 Earlham Street, Norwich. £30

Christ Church Fete. It might be Somerset. £15

Giving a demonstration of the fire engine, Macclesfield. £30

TURNER & THORNTON

PROPRIETOR: A. S. WILLIAMS

WINE AND SPIRIT MERCHANTS

58 MOUNT EPHRAIM - TUNBRIDGE WELLS

ESTAB. 1704   PHONE 280

THE OLDEST WINE VAULTS IN TUNBRIDGE WELLS
FLOOD-LIT FOR THE CORONATION OF GEORGE VI.

Is all that wine still there? £8

There wasn't the traffic in Marlow to be held up then. £30

COAL MINING

Art type	£2-£4
Coal picking	£35-£60
Disasters	£15-£50
Memoriam cards	£15-£20
Memoriam, Gothard	£20-£50
Mines/miners, identified	
photographic	£8-£25
printed	£8-£15
Pit brow lasses	£5-£10
Pithead	£8-£25
Strikes	£25-£50

DELIVERY VEHICLES (identified)

Hand drawn	£10-£30
Horse drawn	£15-£40
Motorised	£15-£40
Mail vans, photographic	£20-£50
printed	£10-£25

DISASTERS

Coastal erosion	£6-£10
Explosions	£6-£30
Fires	£8-£35
Floods	£6-£25
Lightning damage	£8-£25
Memoriam cards	£12-£20
Gothards	£15-£75
Piers	£3-£8
Snow damage	£8-£15
Storm damage	£10-£15
Subsidence	£6-£15
War damage	£6-£12

EVENTS AND PARADES

Country towns	£12-£20
Hamlets/villages	£10-£20
Industrialised towns and cities	£10-£15

FAIRS

Carnivals	£8-£25
Fairgrounds, photographic,	
identified	£25-£40
printed, identified	£8-£15
seaside	£3-£5

in streets, photographic	£20-£35
in streets, printed	£8-£20

FIRE ENGINES (identified)

Horse/hand drawn	£15-£60
Motor driven	£20-£60
Firemen	£8-£15
Fire stations	£8-£40
Oilette	£6
other art types	£3-£6

HERALDIC
Prices quoted are for Town names, others are worth less, overseas countries command a premium.

Early	£4-£6
Other	£1.50-£2.50

INDUSTRIAL

Factories	£5-£8
Machine shops	£3-£6
Mills, cloth	£5-£8
paper	£4-£8
Mining, British, tin, etc.	£15-£35
Mining, overseas	£3-£6
Power houses	£3+
Printing	£3-£8
Saltworks	£25-£45
Shipyards	£4-£12
Steelworks	£4-£8

LORRIES (identified)

Motor, close-up	£15-£60
military	£6-£8
Steam, close-up	£30-£60
military	£15-£20

MAPS

British	£4-£6
Overseas	£3-£6

Cards of an artistic nature, including advertising, can be worth considerably more.

TOPOGRAPHICAL

Fairhaven, Lancashire in 1907. £6

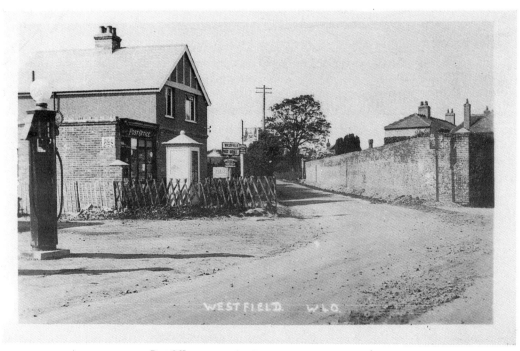

Post Offices are sought after. This one is in Sussex. £20

A road accident 1907 style. £40

Wood Green with a new tram on its way to Cricklewood. £30

A bustling shopping centre. Shinfield, Berks. £15

Two different types of tram dominate this view of Custom House Bridge, Cardiff. £30

MARKETS

Cattle markets	£12-£25
Market places	£4-£15
Street markets, photographic	£8-£25
printed	£6-£12
London, Petticoat Lane	£2+

MOTOR CARS

1930s advertising	£8-£15
1930s photographic	£4-£6
Advertising, early	£8-£15
Advertising posters	£15-£35
Close-up, early photographic	£6-£12
Racing	
Brooklands	£10+
Peking - Paris	£25
others	£6-£15
art type	£4-£6

MOTOR CYCLES

Advertising	£10-£35
Close-up	£6-£8
Racing	
close-up	£8-£15
personalities	£6-£10
comic	£4-£6
With sidecar	£8

PAGEANTS

b&w	£1-£3.50
Coloured	£2-£4
Posters	£6-£8

POST OFFICES

Country towns	
main	£5-£10
sub	£15-£25
Hamlets/villages	£15-£30
Industrialised towns/cities	
main	£2-£4
sub	£15-£20

PUBLIC HOUSES

Country towns	£8-£10
Hamlets/villages	£8-£15

RAILWAY STATIONS

Country towns	
interiors	£25-£35
exteriors	£12-£15
Hamlets/villages	
interiors	£25-£35
exteriors	£12-£20
Industrialised towns/cities	
main and terminii, exteriors	£2-£6
suburban interiors	£25-£35
suburban exteriors	£10-£20

SEASIDE

Bathing huts, close-up	£2-£6
Donkeys	£3-£8
Holiday camps	£1-£5
Pierrot/beach shows	£2-£4
Piers	£1-£6
Punch & Judy	£5-£15
Sandmodels	£2-£5
Superb beach scenes	£5-£8

SHOP FRONTS

Country towns	£20-£30
Hamlets/villages	£15-£25
Industrialised towns/cities	£15-£20

STREET SCENES

Country towns	
animated scenes	£12-£25
general street scenes	£10-£15+
common views	£4-£6+
Hamlets/villages	
animated scenes	£12-£25
general street scenes	£12-£15
common views	£5-£8
Industrialised towns/cities	
animated suburban streets	£10-£20
side streets	£10-£15
common views	£1+

TOPOGRAPHICAL

A period view of the Fox Inn, Greenstreet, Essex. £12

Carriage at Henfield, Sussex. £10

Station Road, Upminster, with some cows being
led to market. £12

Westcombe Park railway station. £30

A fully animated street scene of Bedminster,
a Bristol suburb by Viner of Weston Super Mare. £25

A Tilling-Stevens bus at Maidstone,
its place of manufacture. £40

Established in 1881, this dairy was in East Sheen. £20

Clovelly is normally very common.
This, though, is very unusual. £20

TOPOGRAPHICAL

TARTANS

Tuck	£1.50
Other publishers	75p-£1.50
Tartan-bordered views	50p-£1.50

TRACTION ENGINES

Accidents, photographic	£25-£75
printed	£8-£25
Close-up, photographic	£25-£60
un-identified	£8-£15
Military	£12-£15
Repair gangs	£10-£25

TRAMS

Electric

Track laying	£15-£40
B.o.T. trial runs	£25-£50
opening ceremonies	£25-£50
commemorative cards	£15-£30
close-up	£30-£60
middle-distance	£20-£35
In Memoriam	£8-£15

Horse Drawn

close-up	£25-£60
In Memoriam	£15+

Steam

close-up, photographic	£25-£60
middle-distance photographic	£20-£30
In Memoriam	£8-£15

Miscellaneous

accidents	£12-£40
comic	£1.50-£2.50
decorated	£6-£15
terminii (with trams)	£15-£35
sheds/depots	£15-£25

TROLLEY BUSES

Close-up, early	£12-£25

WATERMILLS

Art types	£2-£4
Close-up, photographic	£6-£15
printed	£4-£8

WINDMILLS

Art Types	£2-£4
Close-up, photographic	£15-£35
printed	£10-£20
Common mills	£2-£6
Disasters	£25-£40
Foreign	£2-£6
Middle-distance, photographic	£8-£15
printed	£6-£12

MISCELLANEOUS

Abbeys	50p-£1
Aerial views	£3-£5
Belgian refugees (WWI)	£10-£15
Bellringers	£10-£15
Bioscopes	£25-£35
Bonfires	£20+
Bridges	£1-£3
Castles	50p-£1
Churches, chapels, etc.	£1.50-£3.50
Cinemas, close-up	£25-£35
Circus sites, British, identified	£25
Comic/greetings, town names	£1.50+
Election canvassing cards	£8+
Election declaration	£10-£15
Manor houses	£2-£4+
Memorials, etc.	£2-£4
Opera houses	£3-£6
Piers/winter gardens	£3-£6
Prisoners of war, etc.	£3-£6
Royal visits	£8-£15
Schools	£3-£6
School groups	£3-£6
Shell damage	£6-£12
Tank banks	£12-£20
Theatres, close-up, photographic	£15-£25
printed	£8-£15
artists impressions	£6+
interiors	£6-£10

ARTISTS

Addison, W.G.	£1
Allan, Andrew.	75p+
Allen, S.J.	50p
Andrews, Eddie	£1-£1.50
Austen, Alex	75p+

TOPOGRAPHICAL

Aveling, S.	£2	Hannaford	75p
Ball, Wilfred	75p	Hayes, F.W.	£2
Barraud, A.	50p	Heyermans, John A.	£1+
Bates, Marjorie C.	£2	Hier, Prof van	50p+
Beer, Andrew	50p	Hodgson, W.Scott	75p
Berkeley, Edith	50p	Hoffman, H.W.	50p+
Blair, Andrew	50p+	Home, Gordon	75p
Blair, John	60p	Hutchinson, F.	75p
Borrow, W.H.	75p+	Jenkins, G.H.	75p
Bothams, W.	50p	Johnson, M.	50p
Bowers, Albert	£1	Johnson, S.	75p
Bowers, Stephen	50p	Jotter	£1.50+
Boyne, T.	75p+	Kammerer, R.	50p
Breanski, Arthur de	£1+	Keene, Elmer	50p
Bridgeman, Arthur W.	75p-£1.50	Keesey, Waler M.	50p
Browne, Tom	£4	Kinnear, J.	75p
Burger, R.	60p	Kirk, A.H.	50p
Burton, F.W.	60p	Lamb, Eric	50p
Bushby, Thomas	£3+	Lauder, C.J.	75p
Carline, George	50p	Lawes, H.	60p
Carruthers, W.	50p	Long, Lady Mary	75p
Cassiers, H.	£4-£6	Longstaffe, E.	£1.50
Clarkson, R.	75p	Lovering, I.	£1.50
Coates, A.	50p	McIntyre, R.F.	75p
Cole, Edwin	75p	Matthison, W.	75p+
Cooper, A.Heaton	£1+	Norman, Parsons	£1+
Cordingley, G.R.	75p	Palmer, Sutton	75p
Corke, C.Essenhigh	50p+	Parr, B.F.C.	50p
Croft, Anne	50p	Payne, Arthur C.	£2-£3
Croxford, W.E.	75p	Penley, Edwin A.	50p
Cubley, H.Hadfield	75p	Percival, E.D.	50p+
Cynicus	£1.50+	Phillimore, R.P.	50p-£4
Diemer, Michael Zeno	£6	Quatremain, W.W.	50p-£1
Douglas, J.	75p+	Quinton, A.R.	£1.50+
Dudley, Tom	75p+	Quinton, F.E.	75p
Dyer, W.H.	50p	Rambler	75p
Dymond, R.J.	50p	Ramsey, George S.	75p
Emanuel, Frank L.	£1+	Richardson, R.W.E.	75p+
Endacott, S.	50p-£1.50	Rousse, Frank	75p+
Finnemore, J.	75p	Rowlandson, G.	£1
Flower, Charles E.	50p -£1.50	Sanders, A.E.	75p
Foster, Gilbert	£1.50	Severn, Walter	50p
Fulleylove, Joan	75p	Shelton, S.	50p
Gallon, R.	50p+	Small, D.	£1.50
Gerald, Brian	50p-£1	Stannard, H.Sylvester	£1
Gozzard, J.W.	75p	Thompson, E.H.	50p
Grant, Carleton	50p	Trick, E.W.	50p
Gretty, G.	50p	Vaughan, E.H.	50p
Guy, T.	75p	Walburn, Ernest	50p

Walker, F.S.	50p
Ward, Vernon	60p
West, Reginald	£1
Williams, Warren	50p+
Wimbush, H.B.	50p+
Wimbush, Winifred	50p
Wright, Seppings	75p
Young, A.	50p
Young, Hayward	£2+
Young, Gwen Hayward	£2+

The artist is J.W. Williams. Scarborough. £1

A.R. Quinton from Tuck series 9535 'Village Crosses'. £5

Warren Williams of Elvet Bridge, Durham
published by Dennis. £1.50

Published by the hotel, this Jotter card
is printed by Burkart. £3

Picadilly Hotel at night by R.H. Penton. £2

POSTCARDS

1995 POSTCARD FAIRS

ALTRINCHAM
CRESTA COURT HOTEL, CHURCH ST.

June 4 • August 6
October 1 • December 3
Admission 30p 10.30 am – 5.00 pm

CHESTERFIELD
**THE WINDING WHEEL
EXHIBITION CENTRE,
HOLYWELL ST.**

July 1 • September 30

Admission 30p
10.00 am – 4.30 pm

CHELTENHAM
RACECOURSE
May 8 • October 27/28

PUMP ROOM
December 28/29

NORTHAMPTON
**THE ABBEY CENTRE, EAST
HUNSBURY (NEXT TO TESCOS)**

June 3 • August 5
October 7 • December 2
Admission Free 10.00 am – 4.30 pm

RF POSTCARDS
17 HILARY CRESCENT, RAYLEIGH, ESSEX
Telephone: 01268 743222

York Card Expo 1996

Friday March 31st 12-8pm
Saturday April 1st 10-6pm
Sunday April 2nd 10-5pm

ARTISTS INDEX

Browne, Stewart	33
Browne, Tom	5,27,33,114
Brundage, Frances	25,42
Brunelleschi	11
Buchanan, Fred	27
Buchell, Charles	33
Bull, Rene	27
Burger, R.	114
Burgess, Arthur	92
Burton, F.W.	114
Bushby, Thomas	114
Busi, Adolfo	11
Butcher, Arthur	25,39
Buxton, Dudley	27

C

C.M.B.	25
Caldecott, Randolph	25
Calland, H.J.	9
Cameron, Archie	27
Cane, Ella Du	41
Carey, John	28
Carline, George	114
Carnel, Albert	28
Carrere, F.O.	39
Carruthers, W.	114
Carter, Reg	28
Carter, Sydney	28
Cassiers, H.	31,92,114
Cattley, P.R.	28
Cauvy, Leon	23
Chalker	28
Chandler, E.	28
Charlet, J.A.	39
Chatterton, F.J.S.	9
Cheret, Jules	23
Cherubini, M.	39
Chidley, Arthur	44
Chilton, G.	11
Chiostri	11
Christiansen, Hans	23
Christie, G. Fyffe	28
Christy, F. Earl	39
Church, Bernard W.	92
Clapsaddle, E.H.	25
Clarkson, R.	114
Cloke, Rene	25
Coates, A.	114

Cobbe, B.	9
Cock, Stanley	28
Colbourne. Lawrence	28
Cole, Edwin	114
Coleman, W.S.	25
Colombo, E.	25,39
Combaz, Gisbert	23
Comicus	28
Cook, C.K.	28
Cooper, A. Heaton	114
Cooper, Phyllis	25
Copping, Harold	39,42,44
Coppola, A.	13
Corbella, Tito	11,39,79
Cordingley, G.R.	114
Corke, C. Essenhigh	114
Cottom, C.M.	25
Cowderoy, K.E.	11,25
Cowham, Hilda	25,28
Crackerjack	28
Craig, Janie	40
Cramer, Rie	11,25
Cremieux, Suzanne	39,44
Croft, Anne	114
Crombie, C.M.	28,103
Crow	28,39
Croxford, W.E.	114
Cubley, H. Hadfield	114
Cumming, Neville	92
Cynicus	28,114

D

Daniell, Eva	23
Dauber	28
Davey, George	28
Daws, F.T.	9
Dawson, Muriel	25
Dexter, Marjorie	25
Diefenbach, K.W.	39
Diemer, Michael Zeno	114
Dinah	25
Dink	103
Dirks, Gus	28
Dixon, Charles	92
Docker, E. Jnr.	23
Donaldini, Jnr.	9
Douglas, J.	114
Drayton, G.	25

ARTISTS INDEX

ARTISTS INDEX

ARTISTS INDEX

GENERAL INDEX

GENERAL INDEX

GENERAL INDEX

Embossed Tuck Easter card from 1905. £6

Warwickshire heavy horse. £7

Attractive Gale & Polden 'History and Traditions'. £6

Unsigned Arthur Thiele cats. £15

WHEN NEXT A LETTER YOU SEND TO ME
LET ME HAVE A LITTLE TEA!

Fred Spurgin at his best. £2.50

No air bag on this Napier car! £25

Sandcastle competition at Redcar. £20

Felling, Durham, 1905. £11

A Welsh choir. £4

The postman from Wark crossing the Tweed. £18

A South Yorkshire mining village. £26

Art Deco at its best in Doncaster. £15

One stop shopping at Otley in the 1930s. £30

Now the gas comes from the North Sea. £15

Attacked by a Zeppelin. £6.50

Against health regulations now. At Durham. £30

Stapylton Villa, 1908. But where?
The steelworks are the clue. £20

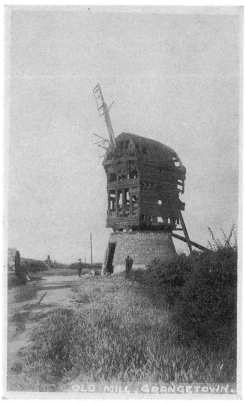
A post mill which last operated in 1878.
Grangetown, Durham. £35

Dinnington circa 1910. £25

1930s Gateshead. Superb. £20